As the Nation's principal
conservation agency, the
Department of the Interior
has basic responsibilities for
water, fish, wildlife, mineral,
land, park, and recreational
resources. Indian and Territorial
Affairs are other major concerns
of America's "Department of
Natural Resources." The
Department works to assure the
wisest choice in managing all
our resources so each will make
its full contribution to a
better United States—now
and in the future.

PLANTS/PEOPLE/AND ENVIRONMENTAL QUALITY

a study of

PLANTS AND THEIR ENVIRONMENTAL FUNCTIONS

published by the

U.S. Department of the Interior,

National Park Service,

Washington, D.C.

in collaboration with the

American Society of Landscape Architects Foundation

Text and Photography by

GARY O. ROBINETTE / Executive Director,

American Society of Landscape Architects Foundation

1972

712
R55

foreword

Although we depend on nature for our survival, most of us lack understanding of the ways in which living plants support our life and can improve its condition. How welcome, therefore, is this book on the function of plants to meet our needs and bring us pleasure, and on methods for evaluating their various usefulness. I thank the American Society of Landscape Architects Foundation and the Department of the Interior's National Park Service, that have worked jointly on this important publication, for showing us so well the ways in which plants can improve the condition of man.

Rogers C. B. Morton,
Secretary of the Interior

preface

For generations Walt Whitman's comment has been the prevailing attitude in the western world concerning natural things including trees—and all vegetation. "We must not know too much, or be too precise, or scientific about birds, and trees, and flowers, and watercraft; a certain free margin, and even vagueness—perhaps ignorance, credulity—helps your enjoyment of these things." Yet today those same elements are more in danger of destruction and are more vital than ever before.

Philip Johnson, the eminent architect, tells us: "Classical economics emphasizes by its very nature what is quantifiable. If you can make a statistic about something it exists. If a thing is not a number it cannot exist."

Beauty in form, color, or texture of plant materials is usually within the province of poets, painters, and philosophers. It is true that there are some things about plants not quantifiable. On the other hand, certain things are measurable. Functional purposes served by plants in control of environmental quality may be measured and, in fact, have been measured by many scientists over the years. What plants do functionally and their effectiveness are of inestimable value to those who use plant materials in a crowded contemporary environment.

The landscape architect has a primary responsibility for the use of plant materials. Recognizing this, the American Society of Landscape Architects Foundation has gathered data drawn from a variety of disciplines relative to the uses of plants.

We welcome this opportunity to work with the National Park Service to publish and distribute this information because of their vital interest in the environment and its preservation. It is our hope that through this cooperation this information will be organized, compiled, illustrated, and given wide distribution for the first time. It is intended that the information contained in this publication will assist educators, designers, administrators, and environmentalists in significant ways. It is also hoped that by indicating what has been done in various fields in this regard, new research will be stimulated to increase our knowledge as to the effectiveness of vegetation in environmental amelioration.

Campbell E. Miller,
President,
American Society of
Landscape Architects
Foundation

introduction

Plant materials have altered very little through human history, but our perception of them has changed with our growing need for their protective company. Once, in the beginning, we were grateful simply for their productivity. We soon learned to love their beauty and that beauty becomes increasingly important as we find fewer flowers and trees to jewel and canopy our lives. One "yesterday" we realized the role of plants in building and holding soil, in controlling moisture, in transmuting air. Having learned to manipulate plant materials to our sustenance and delight, we now do so also to soothe, buffer, and heal those conditions that degrade and even threaten our existence.

Parks, those special realms where vegetation can reign for our observation and enjoyment, are often the only green places we have left amid the grey: oases of beauty in an environment stripped and thronged and dinning. Parks, then, not only care for plant life to preserve needed beauty and recreation which they afford, but with great diversity help also to wall out ugliness and ward off or ease the noxious consequences of our civilization. Indeed, park people have in many ways become uniquely experienced in understanding not only the esthetic values of vegetation, but also the palliative, remedial, restorative benefits as well.

Much of the scientific information provided in *Plants, People, and Environmental Quality* has been used by the National Park Service in its history of administering the National Park System of the United States for the inspiration, enjoyment, and health of mankind. We are proud to join with the American Society of Landscape Architects Foundation in publishing knowledge that may guide the use and preservation of plant materials for a better environment.

George B. Hartzog, Jr.
Director,
National Park Service

contents

plants and
contemporary
culture

Except for the introduction and discovery of some new and exotic varieties and species, plants have remained substantially unchanged throughout history. Ginkgo trees, which probably evolved during an era of volcanic activity and whose descendants once shaded dinosaurs, now have descendants lining the edges of streets and shading automobiles.

In an increasingly manmade world, plants are the unchanging components in an environment. One can see the anachronisms that some plants have become, particularly where development has occurred or the character of an area has undergone a series of changes. Trees, now 50 to 100 years old or older —adjacent to six- and eight-lane, major urban thorough-fares—may have been planted when the roads were at best dusty gravel and with a single lane. The same trees, now grown to maturity, have had part of their roots cut by ditches for water, sewer, and gas lines; have been covered by streets and sidewalks; have had part of their crowns trimmed for overhead power lines, roots removed to make way for foundations and sub-cellers, and the sod over the remaining roots replaced with paving stones. Horse-and-buggy traffic was first displaced with electric trolleys, then with buses, trucks, and automobiles. Gasoline and diesel internal-combustion engines powering each of these vehicles release unburned hydrocarbons and other contaminants into the atmosphere. Buildings shade the trees and bricks cover their roots. Yet the trees still stand, taking what water and nutrients they can from the sun and the little soil remaining, and exchanging oxygen for carbon dioxide.

ATTITUDES TOWARD PLANTS

The culture has changed! The frantic activity of the contemporary, bustling metropolis and the scattered suburbs has little relationship to the slower pace of life and the predominantly rural character of earlier times. Attitudes toward plants are changing, too—but not as fast as our culture. As a result, contemporary environmental designers and planners have generally ignored plants and made little or no serious provisions for their use in large-scale planning, because of the "garden-esque" stigma carried over from earlier eras.

In this increasingly objective culture, the attitude toward plants has tended to remain subjective. Nearly everything else in the contemporary culture is qualified, quantified, measured, and has an economic value placed upon it or its use, while plants are primarily used to enhance a building, beautify a site, or improve the esthetic qualities of an area.

The use of plants should have more importance attached to it for plants can be objectively evaluated and quantified. They must be used for the functions they are capable of performing —functions which have not always been understood, but which do make the environment more desirable.

Research, primarily in the use of plants for acoustic and climatic control, has made it possible to begin to measure and evaluate these and other functions; however, more research is needed.

The major problem is not the lack of knowledge of functional capabilities—but it is the dissemination of known facts. In this way, attitudes toward plant use will become more objective and the functional capabilities of plants will become an important part of our culture.

Existing cultural attitudes are ambivalent, wavering between subjective feelings and the realization that plants are important for the physical role they play, which is keeping our environment in balance. A subjective feeling of reverence may be felt in the midst of a cathedral-like grove of trees. At the same time, the potential of the grove to exchange carbon dioxide for oxygen, to lessen noise, or to reduce airborne pollution, may also be experienced.

Ambivalent cultural attitudes are reflected when what could be a forest giant is placed in a concrete pot and left to grow along an urban avenue with no chance of its ever maturing. This kind of an attempt to bring nature into an urban setting reflects the dichotomy between cultural needs and attitudes.

The needs are for full-size trees and quantities of plants to enhance the environment because of the functions they perform, and to preserve and protect the existing large specimens growing in our urban areas. Also needed is the appreciation of their economic value, so that they may be equated and weighed against conflicting uses which would cause them to be removed or severely mutilated.

Cultural attitudes have not caught up with cultural needs. The attitude toward plants may never really become distinct because it reflects the many and varied attitudes of those individuals who make up our society. People revere, ignore, neglect, and destroy plants, and thus cultural attitudes may be "read" by observing how plants are treated. In our sophisticated cities reverence is reflected by use of large plantings of well-maintained trees and other plants. By ignoring and neglecting plants, and trees in particular, the anachronisms mentioned earlier are recognized; they are proof that the culture placed the care and preservation of these trees very low on its list of priorities—so low, in fact, that the trees were sentenced to a sure death.

The careless destruction and mutilation of plants and trees at any construction site is perhaps the best indicator of our current cultural attitude toward nature in general. Trees and plants compete for physical space with manmade structures. Their preservation and maintenance require expenditure of more time and money than may be available. Since attitudes toward nature are carry-overs from an earlier era, nature is still thought of as something to be conquered or exploited. Hence the attack with chain-saws and bulldozers is usually the first indicator that construction is about to begin. Abraham Kaplan, the philosopher, states it very well when he says:

We have no emotional investment in nature, no identification with it. We stand apart from it and feel free to do as we choose with respect to it.

. . . such a really large part of our environment—for most of us, effectively all of it—is something that was made by other people who presumably had certain purposes, certain ideas, certain ends. And because of their humanity, we are impelled toward a sense of identification or kinship. The environment was made without consulting me, and without allowing for any possibility of my development in it. So I regard as the first problem a restoration of the sense of nature; or, for my part, I would be equally content to say a restoration of the sense of divinity, or the sense of something in the relationship between man and this world not of his making.[1]

[1]Abraham Kaplan, *31 Minds Explore our Environment*, Report of the Committee on Environmental Design, National Association of Home Builders (Wash., D.C., 1965), p. 4.

[2]Morton and Lucia White, *The Intellectual Versus the City* (New York, 1964), p. 12.

As the environment becomes increasingly manmade, plants become more significant as reminders that man is really a part of nature rather than separated and aloof from it. Cultural attitudes are indicators that man remains a stranger in his own environment. If this is true, the question arises, can he relate to trees and plants? If he cannot, are trees in the city relevant? Are any trees relevant in the contemporary culture? In seeking these answers, we must remember that cultural attitude is reflected in the care of trees and plants.

PLANTS/SYMBOLIC AND FUNCTIONAL

Trees and plants serve as symbols, have substance, and perform functions. They are cultivated and cared for because they are symbols of our ancestry—because, we are told, we came from trees; we came from the woods and forests; we came from the land.

In their book, **The Intellectual Versus The City,** Morton and Lucia White have said, "Men live in the cities but dream of the countryside." [2] An attempt is made to bring the countryside into the city and symbolically it may be accomplished with the ginkgo trees lining the edges of streets and with the forest giant placed in a concrete pot. These are attempts at providing an antidote to our loss of contact with the environment.

Plants need to be cultivated and cared for because of the functions they perform. They help provide positive solutions to the many problems existing in our contemporary environment:

☐ Air pollution blocking the sun and changing our climate.
☐ Noise pollution affecting our hearing.
☐ Bright, artificial lighting, and sun glare reflected from glass and metal automobiles and buildings, affecting our vision.
☐ Unpleasant temperature variations in our urban deserts, leaving the city streets too hot, too cold, or too windy.
☐ Soil erosion polluting our rivers.
☐ Headlight glare blinding oncoming drivers.
☐ Floodlights from ballfields and shopping centers shining into houses and backyards.
☐ Vast and impersonal outdoor areas, inhuman and unpleasant and consequently unused.

☐ Areas unused because of a lack of privacy.
☐ Views of junk or ugliness assaulting our eyes while walking or riding.

Functions performed by plants can be categorized and evaluated to help man solve his environmental problems. Plants are among the most effective air-conditioners. They remove carbon dioxide and other pollutants from the air and release oxygen for man's use. Plants trap dust. They release moisture into the atmosphere. Scientists have found that a beech tree, each year, consumes and transforms carbon dioxide from the air in an amount equivalent to that found within the space of 800 single family houses. The leaves, branches, roots, and litter of the plants deter the erosion of soil into creeks, rivers, and streams, thus reducing the pollution of waterways.

Studies are now being conducted to ascertain the effectiveness of plants in reducing the excessive noises in our environment. Turf planted on the banks of a depressed expressway reduces traffic noise. A 2-foot-thick cypress hedge reduces noise by four decibels. Plants reduce sounds of higher wave lengths, those most offensive to the human ear.

Buffer plantings surrounding ugly views or between unrelated land uses give effective privacy even in the most crowded city conditions. The functional capabilities of plants are sufficient to justify their existence in our cities. They are a part of the natural environment, the life support system needed to keep our culture viable.

The major problem facing our culture is our environment and our attitudes toward plants and their uses. These issues are too massive to alter or easily control, and too large to grasp. As a result, individuals turn to those things they can understand, personally relate to, or comprehend. They imagine they have captured nature when they buy a small tree, an encapsulation of ecology in a 5-gallon can, for $1.98.

Cultural attitudes are such that at present we are neither controlling industrial development necessary for human life, nor preserving an essential ecological balance. So we rationalize this by planting 2-inch trees along our new avenue and feel mollified, thinking we have brought nature into our cities.

How does all this relate to environmental design professions which have traditionally been charged with the use of plant material? The dichotomy of frustration, tragedy, trauma, and comedy is felt by designers. However, to overcome this, environmental designers must look at plants in new ways and be provided with additional data to utilize plants functionally, and thereby attempt to solve our environmental problems.

functional
uses of plants

COMPLEX COMPONENTS

Plants are among the most complex components that any designer uses—complex because they are living, growing things, changing with each season. Traditionally their primary use has focused on their esthetic qualities and beauty. Therefore, the designer does not consider their use in the same way as he does wood, steel, and masonry.

The attitudes which govern the designer's use of plants are inexorably intertwined with human history and culture. As culture has changed, some of the attitudes toward the use of plants have changed. Plants as sculptural elements and screens of unsightly views illustrate new uses. Yet, predominant attitudes governing their uses are still subjective.

In a changing environment which is rapidly becoming urbanized and denaturized, cultural values are becoming increasingly objective, qualifiable, and quantifiable. Economic values are placed upon things and their uses. Plants, where used subjectively by the designer are not capable of being quantified, nor are their uses capable of being evaluated and compared to other objective values in the contemporary culture. Consequently where decisions are to be made whether or not to preserve existing trees, or parks, or plant new trees, there is little or no basis for the objective comparison of the values involved and plants are sacrificed for other manmade facilities. Thus the dilemma of the designer is that he needs a system to set in order and sort out the functional uses of plants from other complexities so that they may be evaluated and used intelligently.

"We all know what trees are, of course—and certainly we know what they look like, and how and where they live, how big or small they can be, how old, how fast, or slowly they grow—we know all about trees. Hah! What pompous pipsqueaks we humans can be at times!" [1]

—Russ Kinne

Plants have botanical and horticultural growth characteristics, which have been amply classified over the years by scientists.

Plants have relevant design characteristics, such as form, color, and texture, used by designers and chronicled by poets, paint-

ers, photographers, and philosophers. They also have functional characteristics which affect the environment. In the midst of tentative terminal terracide the average plant user has a subjective rather than objective attitude toward their effective functional capabilities.

What kind of system is necessary to understand the functional uses of plant materials? A plant is part of the environment, is acted upon by the environment, and acts upon the environment. This is true whether in a complex urban, surburban, or rural environment. Plants ameliorate the physical harshness of the contemporary environmental milieu.

These functions should be delineated in breadth and depth. When they are identified, the plant's performance level may be quantified.

DEVELOPING A VOCABULARY

Edward T. Hall, in developing a system to evaluate cultural communications, refers to the parts of language as *isolates, sets,* and *patterns.*[2] To apply this concept to a discussion of the functional uses of plants may work as follows: the obviously unrelated functional uses of plants, such as their ability to control sound, to curtail erosion, to articulate space, to give privacy, to block wind, and to lessen the effects of solar radiation have, in themselves, little form or pattern. These isolated, seemingly unrelated facts are the isolates or the words of a possible vocabulary for classifying functional uses of plants.

Finding an organizational pattern of the ways plants are used functionally, means finding a cohesive, binding force. Phrases begin to develop when we say that plants can be used for architectural, for engineering, for esthetic, or for climatic purposes. When plants are used for privacy control, for screening, for spatial articulation, or for the progressive realization of a view or an object, it is possible to say that these plants are used architecturally. Therefore, the architectural uses of plant materials become a set in the language.

The pattern, or the sentence, would be the entire concept of the functional uses of plant materials. Since plants have architectural uses, engineering uses, esthetic uses, and climatological uses, it is possible to organize a basic language for their

[1] Russ Kinne, review of *Trees,* by Andreas Feininger, Book review in *Popular Photography* (June, 1969), p. 64.

[2] Edward T. Hall, *The Silent Language* (Greenwich, 1956), p. 99-126.

functional use. The functions of plants are the most objective and easily classified of all information regarding them.

This language orders and organizes existing beliefs while indicating present voids in either usage or knowledge, and points the way to future research. It provides a rational handle to grasp an illogical subject fraught with romance, and a framework or basis for the use of natural elements in a highly objective, manmade environment. It communicates facts concerning plant uses and provides a base for compilation of further knowledge.

USES

The functions of plants should be the basis for their use in environmental design. We are selling plants short when we use them for beautification only. The primary aim of planting design should be to use plants in solving environmental problems. Basic to this is a knowledge of their characteristics, what functional problems they solve, and how effectively they solve them. This book has been prepared as a guide for those who desire a better understanding of the functions of plants in the environment.

Architectural Uses

Plants, singly or in groups, form walls, canopies, or floors of varying heights and densities; these are architectural characteristics. In designing buildings, the architect uses materials such as wood, masonry, steel, or concrete, to give privacy, to

SCREENING OBJECTIONAL VIEWS

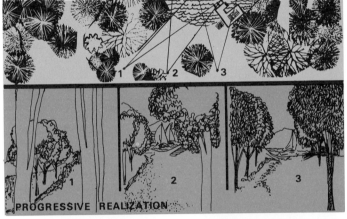
PROGRESSIVE REALIZATION

PRIVACY CONTROL

SPACE ARTICULATION

screen, to progressively reveal a view, or to articulate space. He asks: Is an area too vast for comfortable human use? Should privacy be given to the users of an area? Is there an unsightly area to be screened? Should a significant view be progressively revealed so as to make it more interesting? The planting designer answers these questions by using plants architecturally for these purposes.

Engineering Uses

The engineer is primarily concerned with glare, traffic, and sound control; air-conditioning, or filtration; and soil erosion. Our world becomes more dazzling and glittering daily with the glass and metal of automobiles, building materials, signs, and other shiny objects. When plants are well chosen and judiciously placed, they can control natural and manmade glare and reflection. They also may direct and guide automotive, animal, and pedestrian traffic. Little study has been done in determining the effectiveness of plant materials in softening or muffling sounds in our increasingly noisy environment. Preliminary examination points to the fact that plants can effectively do this. It is a known fact that plants absorb noxious gases, act as receptors of dust and dirt particles, and cleanse the air of impurities. As air pollution increases, the importance of plants becomes increasingly apparent. Plants deter soil erosion by the cover they provide and the spread of their root systems. Further research is underway regarding the value of plants in controlling soil erosion.

GLARE REDUCTION

ATMOSPHERIC PURIFICATION

ACOUSTICAL CONTROL

GLARE REDUCTION

TRAFFIC CONTROL

Climate Control

Shade trees, windbreak trees, and snowfence plants are examples of plants used for climate control. It is well known that plants alter adverse microclimates, making the environment more pleasant and livable for man. However, extensive quantitative studies are necessary to ascertain the degree to which this occurs.

This change is effected through interception of precipitation and solar radiation and through wind and temperature control. In the daytime, the ground temperature in a forest may be as much as 25° cooler than the top of the tree canopy. A vine-covered wall is cooler than a bare wall. Evergreen trees planted close to a wall of a building will create a dead-air space, and insulate the building from abrupt temperature changes. Plants at the base of slopes create a cold air or frost pocket.

Deciduous trees screen the hot sun in summer, and in winter allow warming rays to pass between bare branches. Because snow will not melt as rapidly on the north side of tall evergreens, they can be used in such places as ski slopes to delay snowmelt. Plants can increase, decrease, or direct wind.

Esthetic Uses

Esthetics has generally been the prime factor determining plant use. A plant, whether specimen, topiary, bonsaied, or wind-carved, is effective as a piece of sculpture in creating interest. Placed against a plain wall, a plant with an interesting branching pattern presents a pleasing display of line. A hedge serves as an ever-changing backdrop against which to display other landscape elements. As our world becomes more crowded with manmade objects, plants can be used to blend together various unrelated elements, such as buildings, utility structures, or inharmonious land usages. In addition to their inherent beauty, plants enhance urban surroundings by attracting such natural elements as birds and other animals.

ENFRAMEMENT

PATTERN, REFLECTION & SILHOUETTE

UNIFYING DIVERGENT ELEMENTS
INTRODUCING NATURAL ELEMENTS

ENHANCING OR COMPLEMENTING
ARCHITECTURE

LINE-CALLIGRAPHY

SCULPTURE

DECORATIVE WALL

BACKGROUND

ATTRACTING BIRDS
OR OTHER ANIMALS

SOFTENING
ARCHITECTURE

Other Uses

Other uses which will not be elaborated upon in this book, but which the reader may wish to consider are: appreciation and identification of plants; recreational use such as climbing in or playing on; conservation to supplement organic materials in the soil and provide food and cover for birds and other animals; and supplying food for humans.

architectural uses of plants

ARCHITECTURAL ELEMENTS

Wood and wood products, masonry, concrete, and metal are used by the architect to give shelter, warmth, and protection. They are used to direct, filter or block views. Plants are used in much the same way to form architectural elements. Though they do provide a feeling of shelter and protection, more importantly, they direct, filter, or block views. Under the canopy of a shade tree, one senses a feeling of shelter. Children who play hide and seek behind tree trunks and bushes enjoy the feeling of concealment. Vistas and panoramas are enjoyed more when first glimpsed through openings and then revealed in their entirety. Hedges of plants may be used to screen undesirable views of junkyards or desirable views of bikini-clad beauties sunbathing.

Basic to the planting designer is an understanding of plants as architectural material. It is easy to walk on turf (the floor), under the canopy of a shade tree (the roof), but it is difficult to see through a hedge (the wall). These ideas provide an elementary understanding of the functional uses of plant materials as architectural elements.

ARCHITECTURAL POTENTIALS

The fact that a single plant has bulk and occupies space and when grouped or mixed with other plants forms larger masses, provides the environmental designer with a whole range of architectural potential. The options and capabilities of this potential are endless.

Comprehending the architectural potential of plant material, however, is not synonymous with knowing how plants are to be used. The architectural use of plants merely recognizes that plants have a potential to achieve a given form, texture, color, and size, in a given time, under the proper conditions of growth.

Whether a plant or group of plants actually achieve the architectural potential desired depends upon the designer's selection of plants that can respond to the specific growth conditions. If the wrong plants are selected, or the conditions of growth are not uniform, or are altered in some way, then the architectural potential envisioned by the designer cannot be achieved. However, if the right plants are used and growth conditions are right, then the result will be pleasing for both the designer and the user. It is not intended that this discussion cover description of individual plants and their characteristics, for other sources give this information in detail. The purpose of this discussion, however, is to provide the planting designer with a basic understanding of how plants can be used as architectural elements.

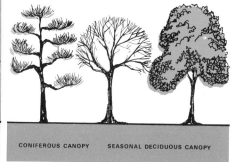

CANOPY   CONIFEROUS CANOPY   SEASONAL DECIDUOUS CANOPY

The single plant may form a canopy of varying height depending upon the type and age of plant.

The canopy formed by a deciduous tree changes from winter to summer. The canopy formed by a coniferous tree is relatively unchanging during the year.

CLOSELY SPACED PLANTS CREATE WALLS

A single plant appears as an object, while the same plants spaced closely together in a line create a wall.

SEASONAL DECIDUOUS WALL   CONIFEROUS WALL

GROUND COVERS FORM FLOORS

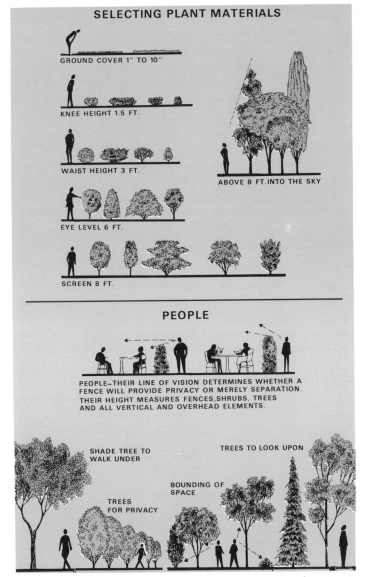

GROUND COVER 1" TO 10"

KNEE HEIGHT 1.5 FT.

WAIST HEIGHT 3 FT.

EYE LEVEL 6 FT.

SCREEN 8 FT.

ABOVE 8 FT. INTO THE SKY

The quality and density of the wall depend on the season of the year for a deciduous tree, but remain substantially uniform for a coniferous tree.

Low-growing plants, when used in a mass, form a floor or ground cover.

When used in combination in the landscape, groups of plants form canopies, walls, or floors of vastly varying texture, height, and density.

PEOPLE

PEOPLE—THEIR LINE OF VISION DETERMINES WHETHER A FENCE WILL PROVIDE PRIVACY OR MERELY SEPARATION. THEIR HEIGHT MEASURES FENCES, SHRUBS, TREES AND ALL VERTICAL AND OVERHEAD ELEMENTS.

SHADE TREE TO WALK UNDER

TREES TO LOOK UPON

BOUNDING OF SPACE

TREES FOR PRIVACY

WALLS   THE INDIVIDUAL'S RELATIONSHIP TO SHRUBS DETERMINES THE BEST HEIGHT FOR A PARTICULAR PLANTING. ANKLE HIGH TO COVER THE GROUND, KNEE HIGH FOR DIRECTION, WAIST HIGH FOR TRAFFIC CONTROL AND PARTIAL ENCLOSURE.

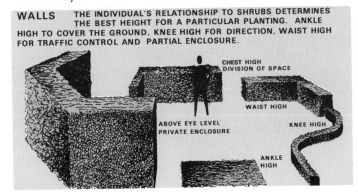

CHEST HIGH DIVISION OF SPACE

WAIST HIGH

ABOVE EYE LEVEL PRIVATE ENCLOSURE

KNEE HIGH

ANKLE HIGH

The ultimate height of plants is an important consideration in determining their possible architectural potential.

Type, age, and condition of the plant determine the degree to which an individual plant filters or blocks a view. Spacing, density, volume, height, and width of the planting determines the degree to which a group of plants filter or block a view.

A single plant standing alone may block or interrupt a view. A group of plants, planted in sequence, may form a wall which blocks or screens a view. Plants, because they are alive, are of variable and dynamic density and character—growing and changing daily, seasonally, and yearly. The variability, density, and character of "walls, ceilings, or floors" formed by growing plants is determined by the density, height, volume, and width of the individual plants which make up the architectural element.

Spacing of the individual plants when used in a mass or group determines the opacity, translucency, or transparency of the massed planting.

The inherent character of plants, coupled with their predictability of form and growth-rate, enables environmental designers to select plants according to the density of the walls, canopies, or floors which they will form.

A grouping of a single variety or a grouping of plants having similar form and density may be used to create a uniform screen to filter a view. A grouping of mixed plants with different forms, shapes, densities, and heights, can produce an infinite variety of degrees of view filtration.

The form, texture, color, and density of a plant, as well as the manner in which it is used, determine the ability of a plant or a mass-planting to become an architectural element. Plants may stand alone, may be grouped with others of the same variety, or may be grouped with other varieties, in endless combinations, to form architectural elements.

Since plants have architectural potential, and can be used to create architectural elements, their functions may be categorized as using them for space articulation, for screening, for privacy control, and for progressive realization of an object, activity, or event. A brief description of the functions, reveals that space articulation is "room-making," privacy control is "enclosure," screening is "view blockage," and progressive realization is "enticement or tantalization."

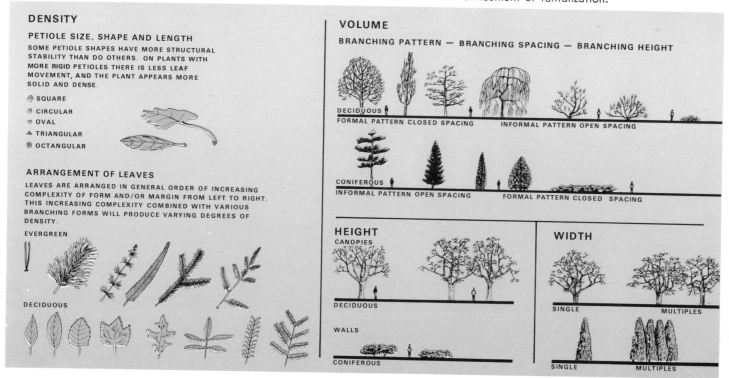

DENSITY

PETIOLE SIZE, SHAPE AND LENGTH
SOME PETIOLE SHAPES HAVE MORE STRUCTURAL STABILITY THAN DO OTHERS. ON PLANTS WITH MORE RIGID PETIOLES THERE IS LESS LEAF MOVEMENT, AND THE PLANT APPEARS MORE SOLID AND DENSE.

◈ SQUARE
◉ CIRCULAR
⊖ OVAL
△ TRIANGULAR
◎ OCTANGULAR

ARRANGEMENT OF LEAVES
LEAVES ARE ARRANGED IN GENERAL ORDER OF INCREASING COMPLEXITY OF FORM AND/OR MARGIN FROM LEFT TO RIGHT. THIS INCREASING COMPLEXITY COMBINED WITH VARIOUS BRANCHING FORMS WILL PRODUCE VARYING DEGREES OF DENSITY.

EVERGREEN

DECIDUOUS

VOLUME

BRANCHING PATTERN — BRANCHING SPACING — BRANCHING HEIGHT

DECIDUOUS
FORMAL PATTERN CLOSED SPACING   INFORMAL PATTERN OPEN SPACING

CONIFEROUS
INFORMAL PATTERN OPEN SPACING   FORMAL PATTERN CLOSED SPACING

HEIGHT
CANOPIES

DECIDUOUS

WALLS

CONIFEROUS

WIDTH

SINGLE   MULTIPLES

SINGLE   MULTIPLES

WALLS REPRESENTATIVE PLANTS INDICATING THE RELATIVE DEGREES OF VISUAL DENSITY.
(AT LEAST 6' HIGH)

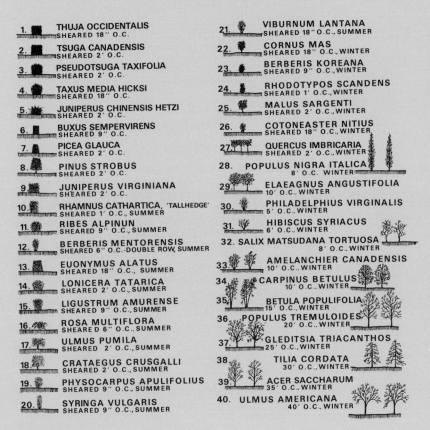

1. THUJA OCCIDENTALIS
SHEARED 18" O.C.
2. TSUGA CANADENSIS
SHEARED 2' O.C.
3. PSEUDOTSUGA TAXIFOLIA
SHEARED 2' O.C.
4. TAXUS MEDIA HICKSI
SHEARED 18" O.C.
5. JUNIPERUS CHINENSIS HETZI
SHEARED 2' O.C.
6. BUXUS SEMPERVIRENS
SHEARED 9" O.C.
7. PICEA GLAUCA
SHEARED 2' O.C.
8. PINUS STROBUS
SHEARED 2' O.C.
9. JUNIPERUS VIRGINIANA
SHEARED 2' O.C.
10. RHAMNUS CATHARTICA, 'TALLHEDGE'
SHEARED 1' O.C., SUMMER
11. RIBES ALPINUN
SHEARED 9" O.C., SUMMER
12. BERBERIS MENTORENSIS
SHEARED 6" O.C.-DOUBLE ROW, SUMMER
13. EUONYMUS ALATUS
SHEARED 18" O.C., SUMMER
14. LONICERA TATARICA
SHEARED 2' O.C., SUMMER
15. LIGUSTRUM AMURENSE
SHEARED 9" O.C., SUMMER
16. ROSA MULTIFLORA
SHEARED 6" O.C., SUMMER
17. ULMUS PUMILA
SHEARED 2' O.C., SUMMER
18. CRATAEGUS CRUSGALLI
SHEARED 2' O.C., SUMMER
19. PHYSOCARPUS APULIFOLIUS
SHEARED 9" O.C., SUMMER
20. SYRINGA VULGARIS
SHEARED 9" O.C., SUMMER

21. VIBURNUM LANTANA
SHEARED 18" O.C., SUMMER
22. CORNUS MAS
SHEARED 18" O.C., WINTER
23. BERBERIS KOREANA
SHEARED 9" O.C., WINTER
24. RHODOTYPOS SCANDENS
SHEARED 1' O.C., WINTER
25. MALUS SARGENTI
SHEARED 2' O.C., WINTER
26. COTONEASTER NITIUS
SHEARED 18" O.C., WINTER
27. QUERCUS IMBRICARIA
SHEARED 2' O.C., WINTER
28. POPULUS NIGRA ITALICA
8' O.C. WINTER
29. ELAEAGNUS ANGUSTIFOLIA
10' O.C., WINTER
30. PHILADELPHIUS VIRGINALIS
5' O.C., WINTER
31. HIBISCUS SYRIACUS
6' O.C., WINTER
32. SALIX MATSUDANA TORTUOSA
8' O.C., WINTER
33. AMELANCHIER CANADENSIS
10' O.C., WINTER
34. CARPINUS BETULUS
10' O.C., WINTER
35. BETULA POPULIFOLIA
15' O.C., WINTER
36. POPULUS TREMULOIDES
20' O.C., WINTER
37. GLEDITSIA TRIACANTHOS
25' O.C., WINTER
38. TILIA CORDATA
30' O.C., WINTER
39. ACER SACCHARUM
35' O.C., WINTER
40. ULMUS AMERICANA
40' O.C., WINTER

CEILINGS REPRESENTATIVE PLANTS INDICATING THE RELATIVE DEGREES OF VISUAL DENSITY.
(SPACED TO GIVE UNIFORM CEILING DENSITY.)

1. THUJA OCCIDENTALIS
AMERICAN ARBOR-VITAE
2. JUNIPERUS VIRGINIANA
EASTERN RED-CEDAR
3. PSEUDOTSUGA TAXIFOLIA
DOUGLAS-FIR
4. ACER PLATANOIDES
NORWAY MAPLE, SUMMER
5. LARIX DECIDUA
EUROPEAN LARCH, SUMMER
6. PICEA PUNGENS
COLORADO BLUE SPRUCE
7. QUERCUS ALBA
WHITE OAK, SUMMER
8. CELTIS OCCIDENTALIS
AMERICAN HACKBERRY, SUMMER
9. ULMUS AMERICANA
AMERICAN ELM, SUMMER
10. FRAXINUS PENNSYLVANICA LANCEOLATA
GREEN ASH, SUMMER
11. QUERCUS ALBA
WHITE OAK, WINTER
12. BETULA POPULIFOLIA
GREY BIRCH, WINTER
13. MACLURA POMIFERA
OSAGE-ORANGE, WINTER
14. QUERCUS PALUSTRIS
PIN OAK, WINTER
15. SORBUS AUCUPARIA
EUROPEAN MOUNTAIN ASH, WINTER
16. CLADRASTIS LUTEA
AMERICAN YELLOW-WOOD, WINTER
17. GINKGO BILOBA
GINKGO, WINTER
18. GLEDITSIA TRIACANTHOS
COMMON HONEY-LOCUST, WINTER
19. RHUS TYPHINA
STAGHORN SUMAC, WINTER
20. ROBINIA PSEUDOACACIA
BLACK LOCUST, WINTER

FLOORS OF EXTERIOR SPACES CREATED BY PLANT MATERIALS RATED BY THEIR ABILITY TO WITHSTAND FOOT TRAFFIC AND THE EASE WITH WHICH THEY ARE ABLE TO BE WALKED UPON.

1. POA PRATENSIS
KENTUCKY BLUEGRASS
2. THYMUS SERPYLLUM
THYME
3. ANENARIA VERNA CAESPITOSA
MOSS SANDWORT
4. ANTHEMIS NOBILIS
CAMOMILE
5. MATRICARIA TCHIHATCHEWII
TURFING DAISY

6. CERASTIUM TOMENTOSUM
SNOW-IN-SUMMER
7. HEDERA HELIX
ENGLISH IVY
8. AJUGA REPTANS
BUNGLEWEED
9. COTONEASTER ADPRESSA PRAECOX
CREEPING COTONEASTER
10. ROSA WICHURAIANA
MEMORIAL ROSE

14

SPACE ARTICULATORS
THE INDIVIDUAL PLANT IS A SPECIMEN IN WHICH, THROUGH SPACING, IT BECOMES FENESTRATION, HEDGES, BAFFLES, TRACERY, CLUMPS, CANOPY.

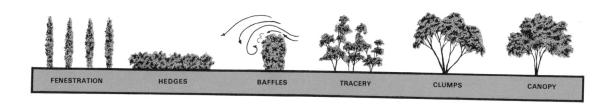

FENESTRATION HEDGES BAFFLES TRACERY CLUMPS CANOPY

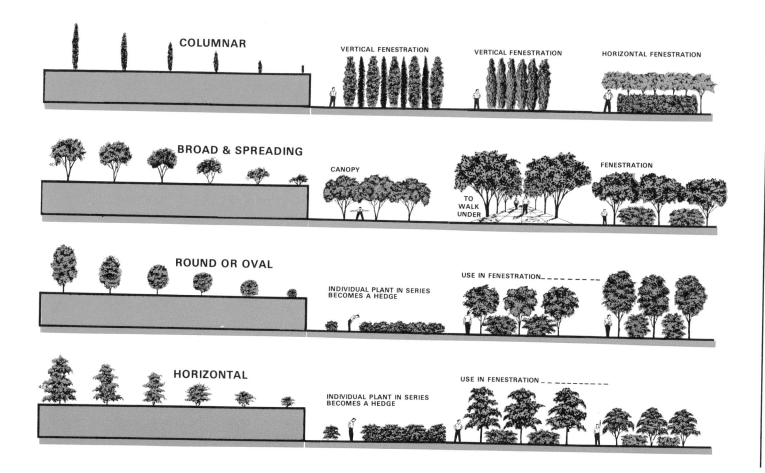

COLUMNAR

VERTICAL FENESTRATION VERTICAL FENESTRATION HORIZONTAL FENESTRATION

BROAD & SPREADING

CANOPY TO WALK UNDER FENESTRATION

ROUND OR OVAL

INDIVIDUAL PLANT IN SERIES BECOMES A HEDGE USE IN FENESTRATION

HORIZONTAL

INDIVIDUAL PLANT IN SERIES BECOMES A HEDGE USE IN FENESTRATION

SPACE ARTICULATION

Any element, natural or manmade, which is able to form a floor, wall, or ceiling, may be used to articulate space. Buildings, walls, fences, earth-forms, rocks, water, plants, and changes in ground elevations are all used to indicate the parameters of external space.

From its hollowness arises the reality of the vessel; from its empty space arises the reality of the building.
—Lao-Tse [1]

Architecture . . . is the beautiful and serious game of space.
—William Dudok [1]

To grasp space, to know how to see it, is the key to the understanding of building.
—Bruno Zevi [1]

Whatever the utilitarian, esthetic or other aims of an architect may be, architecture becomes manifest by the barriers (imaginary or real) enclosing space. A person within this defined space is subject to the subconscious spatial sensation . . .
—Erno Goldfinger [2]

Space Perceived

Factors involved in creating the sensation of space are the space itself and the manmade or natural objects and elements which define or articulate it. Variations in the quantity or the quality of either or both of these two factors are the essence of space modulation or manipulation.

[1] John Ormsbee Simonds, *Landscape Architecture: The Shaping of Man's Environment* (New York, 1961) pp. 84-85.
[2] Erno Goldfinger, "The Sensation of Space," *Architectural Review* (November 1941), p. 129.
[3] *Ibid.*, pp. 128-129.
[4] Michael Leonard, "Humanizing Space," *Progressive Architecture* (April 1969), p. 43.

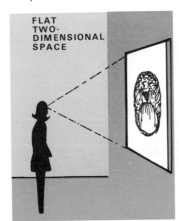

FLAT TWO-DIMENSIONAL SPACE

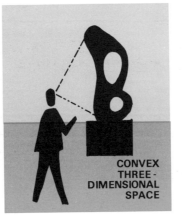

CONVEX THREE-DIMENSIONAL SPACE

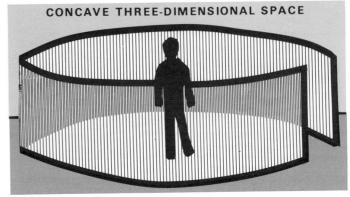

CONCAVE THREE-DIMENSIONAL SPACE

Space is visually perceived three ways, according to Goldfinger. The first of these is flat, two-dimensional space, such as a painting lacking depth. In all pictorial phenomena, space may be depicted or illustrated, but never actually formed. The second of spatial perception is plastic, three-dimensional convex, and is best illustrated by a piece of sculpture. The observer experiences the space from without as he moves around the finite shape viewing three-dimensional relationships stereoscopically. In the case of traditional sculpture, the observer does not move through it, but looks upon its inner-spatial modulation from exterior vantage points. The third type of space perception is three-dimensional concave, kinetic space, which the viewer, from vantage points within the space, experiences and comprehends it subconsciously as spatial sensation; or as Goldfinger phrases it, " . . . when space is enclosed with the skill of an artist . . . then 'spatial sensation' becomes spatial emotion and enclosed space becomes architecture." [3]

According to Michael Leonard, three-dimensional space is divided into two components. Positive space is space contained, with the visual field limited, inner-focused, and static; while negative space is space left over, dynamic, with the visual field unlimited and lacking center focus. According to his idea, positive space is that area inside of a building, and negative space is the exterior area between masses. He states, "Positive space is more static in character and has an inner-focus; negative space is dynamic, for it gives no feeling of center, the visual field is not limited, and there is a sense of expansion outward." [4]

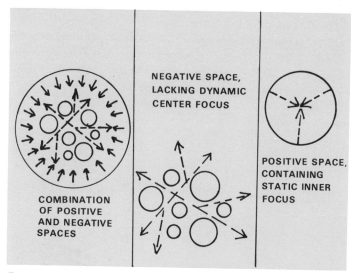

NEGATIVE SPACE, LACKING DYNAMIC CENTER FOCUS

POSITIVE SPACE, CONTAINING STATIC INNER FOCUS

COMBINATION OF POSITIVE AND NEGATIVE SPACES

Exterior space may be either "positive" or "negative," depending upon how it is defined by architectural elements of wood, masonry, metal or plants. Generally, exterior spaces are larger in scale than interior spaces. Exterior space definers or articulators are used in a looser, more informal, manner in keeping with the scale of the exterior spaces and the nature of the material used. A good explanation of the characteristics of exterior spaces and the means of their articulation in a discussion on site space is outlined by Kevin Lynch as follows:

In contrast to architectural space, site space is much larger in extent and looser in form. The horizontal dimensions are normally much greater than the vertical dimensions. Structure is less geometric or demanding, connections less precise, square; an irregularity in plan which would be unbearable in a room may, at the exterior scale, be tolerable or even desirable.

The site-plan uses different materials, notably earth, rock, water, and plants, and is subject to constant change, whether it be the rhythm of human activity and of the natural cycles, or the cumulative effects of growth, decay, and alteration. The light which gives it form shifts constantly with the weather, hour, and season. Most important of all, it is seen, not as a single view, but in sequence over an extended period of time while the observer himself is in motion.[5]

Another author, John O. Simonds, writing on the organization of outdoor spaces in his book **Landscape Architecture**,[6] presents a complete narrative on the evocative qualities of exte-

rior spaces. His discussion covers spatial size and form and qualities of space. A closer examination of the works of the previously mentioned authors will provide more information on why exterior spaces should be broken up or defined.

The purpose of this discussion is to tell how exterior spaces may be defined or articulated with plants. When it is understood that large exterior spaces are usually perceived as negative space having a dynamic quality, and that objects or elements having a three-dimensional "plastic" quality may be introduced to define, encompass, or articulate exterior space, then it is easy to see how plants may be used as sculptural and architectural elements.

Space Defined

Human perception of space is based primarily upon sight. The relative appearance of distance from a viewer to any element which blocks or filters his view begins to create spatial sensations of enclosure. The closer the element, the more intense the spatial sensation becomes. The intensity of spatial sensations is also heightened by the appearance of discernible texture and shades of color on the element. Coarse textures and darker shades appear to advance toward the viewer, while finer textures and light shades appear to retreat.

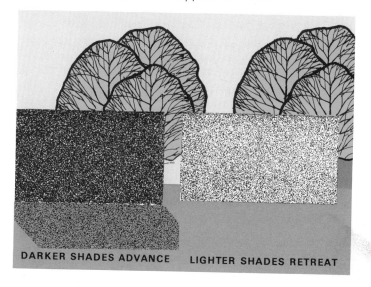

DARKER SHADES ADVANCE   LIGHTER SHADES RETREAT

[5] Kevin Lynch, *Site Planning* (Cambridge, 1962), p. 56.
[6] Simonds, pp. 79-113.

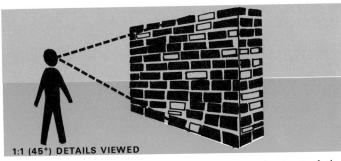

1:1 (45°) DETAILS VIEWED

The area within a 45° cone of vision is about the limit of the human eye to perceive any degree of detail. Beyond this cone, details appear fuzzy. The 45° cone occurs when the viewer is as far from the element being viewed as the element is tall, a distance to height ratio of 1 to 1. At this distance a spatial sensation of nearly full enclosure is felt, particularly if the enclosure is on three or more sides.

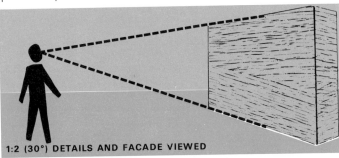

1:2 (30°) DETAILS AND FACADE VIEWED

The 30° cone of vision occurs where the height to viewing distance ratio is 1 to 2. Within the area of the 30° cone, the entire element and its details are perceived clearly. It is at this distance that the spatial sensation of enclosure is at its lowest threshold.

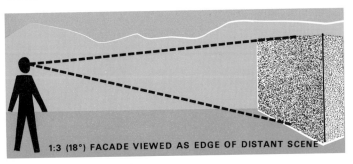

1:3 (18°) FACADE VIEWED AS EDGE OF DISTANT SCENE

When the viewer is far enough away from the element so that cone of vision is decreased to 18°, a height of viewing distance ratio of 1 to 3, only a minimum sense of spatial enclosure is experienced. The element loses detail and its containing quality, and functions as an edge psychologically, providing a sense of place for the viewer rather than a sense of confining space.

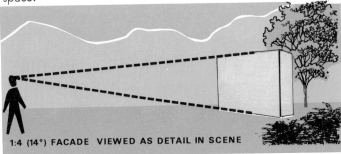

1:4 (14°) FACADE VIEWED AS DETAIL IN SCENE

As the height distance viewing ratio for an element approaches 1 to 4, the cone of vision needed to view the element is only 14°. At this distance the element loses its primary importance and becomes in itself a detail on an edge for the broader scene.

Plants as Articulators

Plants are able to form walls, canopies or floors in the landscape. They are able to articulate, define, enclose or delimit exterior space either by themselves or in conjunction with other landscape architectural components. Plant materials are the objects in the outdoor environment which are absent in architectural interior spaces. They are less well understood or documented as potential space defining elements than are other architectural materials.

The individual plant is able to articulate space by itself and, at times within itself, as when a small boy perched high in the central branches of a weeping willow tree is within the green domed cathedral-like roof and walls formed by the falling branches.

Plants are widely recognized as positive sculptural elements possessing seasonably changing beauty, particularly when they stand alone as specimens. However, these same plants when planted with others may become autonomous parts of larger components which define exciting spaces, through which the users of the landscape move. A series of single plants placed adjacent to one another may form a nearly solid visual barrier and may cover or give edge to an outdoor room.

Since vegetation is dynamic, changing, and growing, plants may not define space as envisioned by their designer until they have reached maturity. They may not be able to form the density of an architectural screen or covering of another material. However, they do have the added advantage of changeableness and seasonal interest.

FLOORSCAPE
CEILINGSCAPE

FACTORS AFFECTING BOTH:
A. AMOUNT OF ENCLOSURE
  1. COMPLETE
  2. BROKEN

B. A RELATIONSHIP BETWEEN:
  1. DENSITY
    a. TRANSPARENT
    b. TRANSLUCENT
    c. OPACITY

2. TEXTURE
  a. FINE
  b. MEDIUM
  c. COARSE

3. SCALE
  a. LARGE
  b. SMALL

SINGLE FORM

SCALE FOR FLOORSCAPE

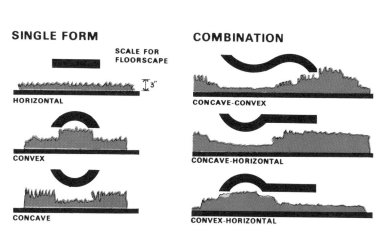

HORIZONTAL

CONVEX

CONCAVE

COMBINATION

CONCAVE-CONVEX

CONCAVE-HORIZONTAL

CONVEX-HORIZONTAL

SINGLE FORM

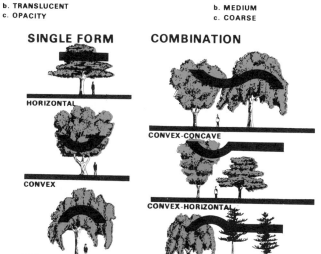

HORIZONTAL

CONVEX

CONCAVE

COMBINATION

CONVEX-CONCAVE

CONVEX-HORIZONTAL

CONCAVE-HORIZONTAL

SCALE

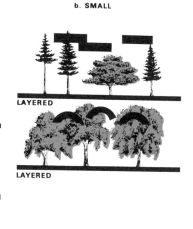

LAYERED

LAYERED

FLOORSCAPES AND CEILINGSCAPES ARE FORMED THROUGH APPLICATIONS OF:
PLANT FORMS, PLANT SCALE, PLANT DENSITY, PLANT TEXTURE, PLANTS IN COMBINATION WITH PLANTS, AND PLANTS IN COMBINATION WITH LANDFORMS.

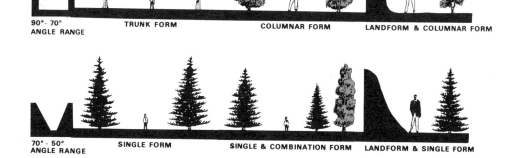

90°- 70° ANGLE RANGE

TRUNK FORM

COLUMNAR FORM

LANDFORM & COLUMNAR FORM

70° - 50° ANGLE RANGE

SINGLE FORM

SINGLE & COMBINATION FORM

LANDFORM & SINGLE FORM

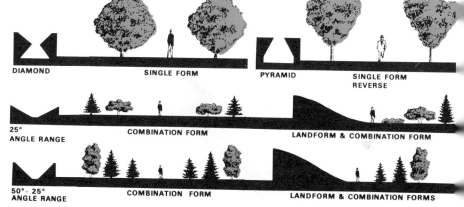

DIAMOND

SINGLE FORM

PYRAMID

SINGLE FORM REVERSE

25° ANGLE RANGE

COMBINATION FORM

LANDFORM & COMBINATION FORM

50° - 25° ANGLE RANGE

COMBINATION FORM

LANDFORM & COMBINATION FORMS

Because plants can control both the size and quality of exterior space, they can control, to a large extent, human perception of the space designed. Plants then articulate space by themselves, with other plants, in conjunction with landforms, in conjunction with buildings, and in conjunction with architectural landscape features such as walls, fences, canopies, and paving.

PLANTS THEMSELVES

MULTIPLE PLANTS

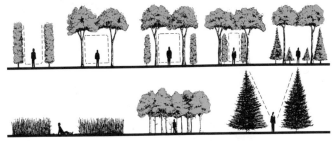

LANDFORMS

EXPANDING LANDFORMS

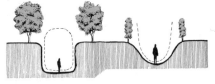

COMPLEMENTING LANDFORMS

NEGATING LANDFORMS

Design Reinforcement

Since most planting plans are formulated near the end of the environmental design sequence, plants must often be adapted to spaces created by other design elements. Plant materials may be manipulated so as to add refinement and subtleties to these spaces which otherwise may be unexciting and lacking in interest. This may best be accomplished by taking into full consideration the ideas and concepts of the original designer and reinforcing them through the use of plants as architectural elements. Some of the techniques which may be used by the planting designer include hierarchal recognition, articulation of elements, modulation, and functional realization.

HIERARCHAL RECOGNITION The original designers conceive a hierarchal order of movement or perception for the viewers or uses of the surroundings which must be taken into consideration and recognized by the planting designers. Once recognized, the hierarchal order is reinforced through the selection and placing of plants to direct movement of people and their vision in the manner intended by the original designers. When the hierarchal order is followed, movement and vision are directed toward the primary spaces first and then to secondary and tertiary spaces.

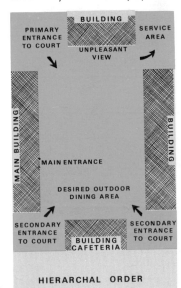

HIERARCHAL ORDER

HIERARCHAL RECOGNITION AND MODULATION

MODULATION

The planting designer uses plants to break down large spaces into smaller, irregular, or rhythmically discernible units. The plants help to establish an awareness of modulated sequence of a series of smaller spaces, rather than one large space. The rationale for modulation is important because it is easier to conceive and perceive an individual unit or a small grouping of units within any sequence than the entire sequence itself. If a space is too large it is incomprehensible to the viewer as a space; however, if divided into a series of smaller spaces, through which the observer moves in a rhythmic pattern, each individual space is easily understood.

ARTICULATION OF ELEMENTS

When a design analysis by the planting designer has revealed essential design components and their individual architectural and spatial elements, then plants may be used to define them clearly. For example, a building entrance may be an architectural element which needs exterior space articulation. Using articulation as a rationale, the planting designer may subdivide large areas into a series of smaller areas.

**ARTICULATION OF AN ELEMENT
(ENTRANCE)**

FUNCTIONAL REALIZATION

The planting designer must understand the functions of spaces intended by the original designer. He must reinforce the functions and interpret them to the users of the spaces through the judicious selection and placing of plants. Larger spaces may have more than one function or functional zone, usually separated and defined by the planting designer. With plants, movement and vision through spaces are controlled so as to give the viewer an easy grasp of an entire space or to present him with a series of smaller spaces within a larger space, on the assumption that smaller spaces are easier to comprehend. Eight design techniques are used to do this: direction, sequential movement, view-step dichotomy, invitation, channeling, pooling, rechanneling, and enclavement.

Direction is accomplished by creating a feeling of mobility within the viewer's mind, encouraging him to move through space or spaces, rather than just viewing them from a static position. Either the plants themselves or their arrangement can pull the observer. The texture, form, and color of plants direct the vision of the observer through the space in such a way that he feels compelled to move on and explore the remainder of the space or spaces.

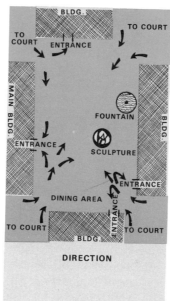

DIRECTION

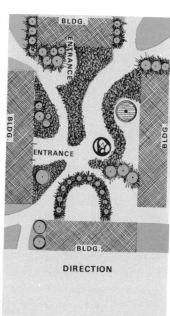

DIRECTION

Sequential movement through a series of smaller spaces which have been subdivided from a larger space enables the observer to experience each of the smaller spaces separately and independently. The actual sequence of spaces may be revealed to the viewer as a whole, but each space should be capable of being experienced as an entity. Sequential movement is most effective when the observer's movement is modulated by varying sizes and shapes as he moves through the space or series of spaces.

View-step dichotomy is the term used to describe the phenomenon which is deliberately created to make one view a space or element within a larger space; but to be unable to go directly to that space or element. It is created where the view is drawn to a point through the use of plants while other plants are used to physically inhibit the observer from reaching the point by a direct route. It is best described as "the eyes go one way while the feet go another."

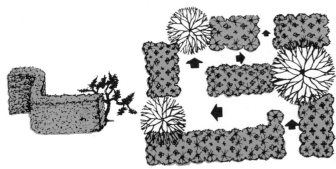

Invitation requires the use of stimulation, attraction, suggestion, or curiosity to pull the observer and make him want to move through a large space or to an element within a space. It is best expressed as a "why don't you come up and see me sometime" design technique. Plants are used to filter, partially hide or tantalize the viewer into wanting to know what is just beyond.

Channeling is creating corridors for funneling fast, active, dynamic movement within a space. It is particularly useful when there is a need to provide a change of pace for better comprehension or perception of an area, or to direct the flow of traffic.

Pooling is the technique of creating a room or resting place at the end of a channel. If the channel is the corridor, the rapids of a narrow, fast-running stream of activity, then the pool is the room for nearly stationary inactivity, a settling basin.

Rechanneling is directing activity from the pool or room back into another channel using direction or invitation. The channeling, pooling, and rechanneling cycle is a technique which may be effectively employed in directing movement and breaking down overly large spaces into discernible units. It is an effective technique for modulating spaces.

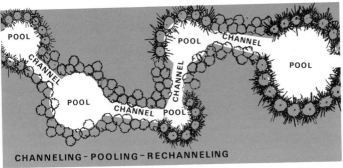

CHANNELING-POOLING-RECHANNELING

Enclavement is the creation or articulation of small spaces which become quiet areas or small eddies out of the mainstream of the flow of traffic. In creating them, plants are used to provide a soothing experience of rest and relaxation. The difference between enclavement and pooling is that with pooling the main traffic slows down as it moves through the pool, while with enclavement, the main traffic flow moves past the space.

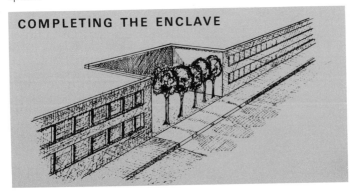

COMPLETING THE ENCLAVE

COMPLETION Occasionally the architect, landscape architect, urban planner, or designer will have begun to articulate spatial relationships which still need completion or complementing near the end of the design sequence. Some spaces are left so large as to make them humanly incomprehensible. The recognition of plants as space-articulating elements for "breaking down" and "finishing off" a space or spaces is essential, if the spaces are to be defined and made positive. The techniques used by the planting designer to accomplish this are closure, containment, enframement, linkage, enlargement, reduction, and subdivision.

Closure is using plants to finish off a space that has been left open. It makes the space more complete and identifiable.

Containment is achieved when the designer provides a space where the user experiences the feeling, "I am in a small space or in one of a series of small spaces, not a large space." This usually occurs when the small space is inside or part of a larger space and is designed in a way so as to focus the user's attention on the small, human-scale feeling of the space. In such a space, the user loses the conscious feeling that the small space is part of a larger space.

Enframement is a technique for drawing attention to the "prime view" or one of the most important spaces in the area. The planting design focuses attention on the desired view or object and away from the larger space in which the view or object occurs.

Linkage is the technique which joins one space with another to make a large area seem smaller and less alien. Linkage makes it appear clear that a smaller space is part of a group of spaces or part of a larger space.

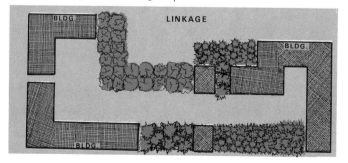

Enlargement is a method of changing the apparent size of a large space by contrasting it to the infinite space of the skyscape, and making it seem smaller by comparison. It involves judicious use of the horizon line and plant materials to direct attention upward rather than to direct attention to the space itself. An example of the technique occurs when a large space formed by vertical building walls is made to appear smaller through the use of plants, creating a cone effect similar to the cone of a volcano. While the space may be visually reduced only slightly, the contrast with the sky will make it appear smaller.

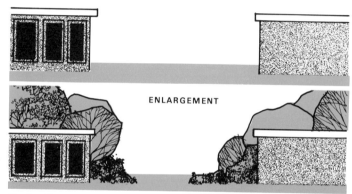

Reduction is accomplished by placing plants in an overly large space to make the space smaller and more comprehensible.

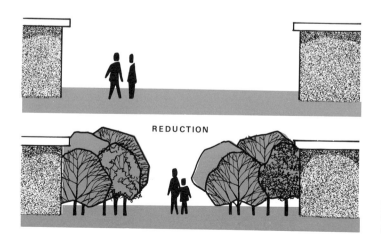

Subdivision is the technique for dividing space either horizontally or vertically to reduce the apparent size of the space. Most exterior space is perceived according to its horizontal dimensions of width and length with little conscious thought being given to its vertical dimension of height. In cases where space is viewed from above or attention is directed upwards by a tall element, such as a building or cliff, the height dimension enters into the perception of space. Vertical subdivision involves using plants to deliberately form walls, dividing the dimensions of length and width of a large space, into smaller spaces. Horizontal subdivision involves using plants to form canopies at various levels creating ceilings when viewed from below, and floors when viewed from above, or even layers if viewed from different heights.

Space articulation, a major function of architectural design, is also vital in the exterior environment. The environmental designer has many materials which can be used to define areas or delimit spaces. Plants are one of these materials which can subdivide space three-dimensionally, and should be employed to a much greater extent. They have seldom been used consciously, rationally, and objectively to perform this function. This is a mere suggestion of the potential of plant use for these functions. It does, however, illustrate the potential uses of these natural materials as space articulators and outlines an approach or way of thinking for the environmental designer to use and deal with plants as units for space delimitation. The same qualities which enable plants to articulate space enable them to make the environment more habitable by performing other functions such as the screening of offensive views.

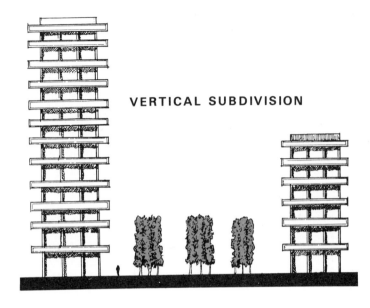

VERTICAL SUBDIVISION

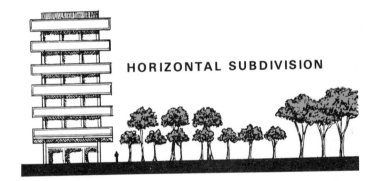

HORIZONTAL SUBDIVISION

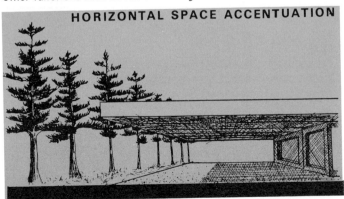

HORIZONTAL SPACE ACCENTUATION

SCREENING
The Need

Manmade development disrupts the natural landscape. Technology has not progressed to the point where construction automatically produces an attractive environment to replace that which has been destroyed. In fact quite the opposite is usually true. As our environment becomes highly developed, some portions of our landscape become increasingly ugly. The physical growth of the institutional facilities of our culture, including large scale construction concomitant with this growth, is unavoidable. These facilities are not always attractive and presentable, from all directions, at all seasons. They are often simply eyesores.

Screening is visually blocking out that which is unsightly with something more harmonious, or at least less offensive. Screening is a means of providing visual control in the landscape through view direction and "negation" of ugliness simply by hiding it. Screening implies isolation, confinement, and concealment of the unwanted, while allowing free access to the remainder of the landscape. Screening has a positive and a negative connotation—positive screening enhances the surroundings, while negative screening blocks ugly surroundings from view.

We are surrounded in our contemporary environment with areas, activities, and objects we would rather not see. We screen or hide these parts of our environment to make them less objectionable and the total environment more acceptable. Typical areas in our contemporary environment commonly screened are: junk yards, service areas and facilities, construction activities, storage areas, parking lots, industrial facilities, electrical transformer yards, power facilities of all types, athletic fields and areas, roadways and driveways, outdoor air-conditioning units, cemeteries, and activities unrelated to the surroundings.

There appears to be a continuum of objectionability ranging from the blatantly ugly, to that which, though not extremely distasteful, is better unseen than seen. Steps in this continuum are objects, areas, or activities which are:

- [ ] downright ugly and repugnant, without redeeming features.
- [ ] offensive, or visually distasteful in a specific area or at a specific time.
- [ ] causes distress when seen at a particular place and/or time.
- [ ] inharmonious to their surroundings.
- [ ] of inferior quality to their general environment. Nothing inherently wrong or ugly about this—it would be better if it were not seen.
- [ ] matters of individual preference, even though there may be nothing objectionable. It is the decision of the designer or owner that they be concealed.

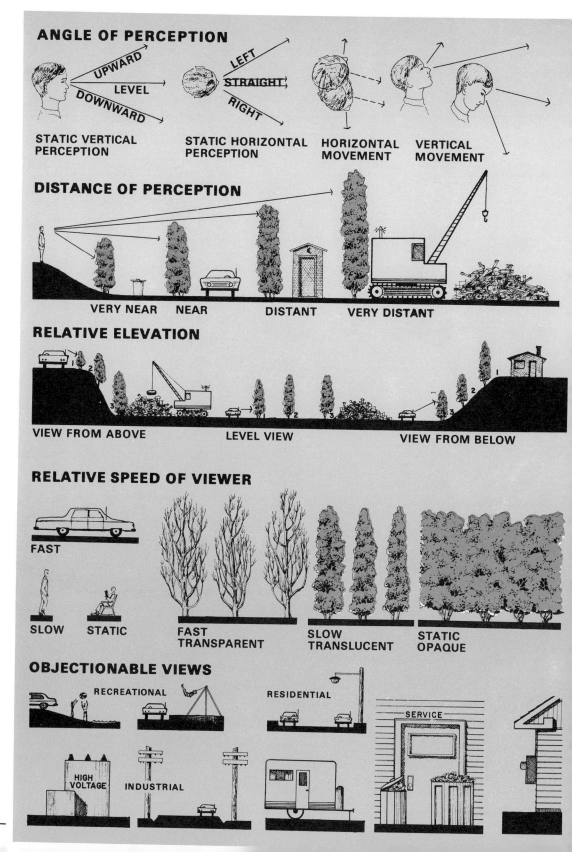

Before regarding the possible ways to screen, it is necessary for the designer to know the size, scale, or extent of the object, area, or activity. Some areas appear to be, or actually may be, more objectionable at certain seasons of the year. Screening must recognize the factor of selective directional blockage of undesirable views. Analysis of the site reveals the direction from which screening is most needed. The angle of view or approach may dictate the sequence or distance of spacing of the elements for effective screening. The speed of movement past an offensive view plays a determining role in the selection of the most effective screening method. Generally, the faster the movement past the view, the more widely the screening materials may be spaced. The height, distance, and location of the viewer is the determining factor in use and placement of a screening element. The rise and fall of topography increases or decreases the height from which a moving person views an object or area.

Plants for Screening

There are myriad materials for the environmental designer's use in creating elements for screening. Some of the elements are architecture, topography, walls, fences, sculpture, water, and plants.

The most ubiquitous environmental screening elements and the ones least analyzed, and categorized or understood, for their effectiveness as screening elements, are plants. Although planting to screen ugliness or objectionable views gained wide acceptance during the highway beautification efforts of the mid-1960's, quantitative data was unavailable to show ways plants can be used to screen and what their limitations are. Available information has not been well cataloged and indexed. Guidance for the designer who would use plants for screens in an ever more crowded and cluttered world of the future is limited. How then, may plant materials be used to do this? What are the factors for consideration in using plants for masking, veiling, or screening?

Even though plants are growing, changing elements, and as such are less dependable and predictable in their density or ultimate form than are fences, walls, or architecture, they may be used in much the same way as any other screening element; they have the benefit of a natural appearance; and they have a rich inherent design characteristic because of their diversity of form, texture, and color.

When plants are used for screening, consideration is given to perceptibility of unsightliness—i.e., how much and what is ugly to an individual; or, where is the offensive view in relation to the viewer; and, what are the limits of the viewer in regard to direction, distance, and mobility. The further away an object is, the larger it must be before it becomes objectionable. On the other hand, a relatively small object close to an observer may be disagreeable and require screening. It goes without saying that a large, distant object requires relatively larger plants for screening. Close objects require denser plantings and/or closer spacing. Because of perceptual capabilities, the size of an object, area, or activity, coupled with its relative distance from the viewer, is the determining principle in screening.

Speed of movement is directly related to width of perceptability. The faster the motion, the narrower the cone of vision. Therefore, an opaque planting screen may be needed to relieve a stationary viewer from unpleasantness. By the same token, the transparency of deciduous trees in winter may be adequate for a rapidly moving viewer. The density of a plant screen may vary from extreme transparency, through translucency, to near opacity.

In summary, screening involves the isolation and sometimes the amalgamation of undesirable aspects for the purpose of obscuring unwanted views while permitting free access to the landscape. Exterior screening may be accomplished with a number of elements, including plant materials. When plants are used for screening, evaluations must be made such as: What needs to be screened? From which direction is it needed? How much or how dense a screen? Is the viewer stationary or mobile? What is the viewer's angle of approach to the unpleasant view? At what season is it most unsightly? Can the viewer be directed to an alternative view in addition to or instead of screening? It is possible to select the type, height, width, and extent of the planting necessary after answering these questions. Then the precise plants may be selected. Plants can do an efficient job of screening ugliness if they are judiciously chosen, placed, and maintained.

PRIVACY CONTROL

It is necessary to differentiate between privacy control and screening. Screening allows free access through the landscape while inhibiting certain views. Privacy control secludes a particular area from its surroundings. Planting for screening is concealing unsightly views, so that the remainder of the landscape may be opened up to unassailed human view.

Planting for privacy control is secluding an area from its surrounding for special use. The same design concepts may be used either for privacy control or screening. The difference depends upon point-of-view and intent of either the viewer or the user.

PRIVACY CONTROL

SCREENING

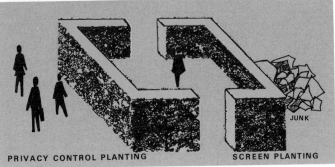

PRIVACY CONTROL PLANTING   **SCREEN PLANTING**

The Need

We live in a crowded world. By the middle of the 21st century, the population will approach 10 billion. Such crowding, attendant to a population of this magnitude, makes indi-

vidual privacy illusory and fragile. Privacy is necessary for survival. It is important to the individual, to the family, or the group; however, outdoor privacy becomes increasingly difficult to provide.

Privacy is needed for such activities as sunbathing, camping, picnicking, reading, relaxation, contemplation, people or nature-watching, and conversation. Privacy may be needed in such places as cemeteries, outdoor theaters, stadiums, patios, courts, and terraces.

When privacy is wanted for the group or the individual, it is wanted from "others" or outsiders such as neighbors, strangers, delivery men, non-related individuals, persons in automobiles, trucks, buses, or cycles, or in some cases—the entire world!

Methods

A hierarchal organization continuum from the most public spaces to the most private has been developed by Serge Chermayeff and Christopher Alexander. The progression is urban public, urban semi-public, group public, group private, family private, and individual private. The transition from one type of space to another providing privacy is accomplished usually by some type of barrier or barriers.

A quote from their book, **Community and Privacy**, may serve to suggest additional ways in which privacy may be maintained, even though a daily interchange of human activity takes place through public to private places.

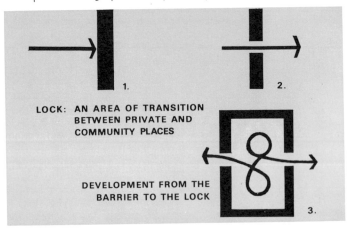

LOCK: AN AREA OF TRANSITION BETWEEN PRIVATE AND COMMUNITY PLACES

DEVELOPMENT FROM THE BARRIER TO THE LOCK

Who and what interferes with what and whom, to what extent, when and how, are significant questions that the urban designer has to ask himself. The conditions where the integrity of each of the adjoining domains must be preserved at all times, in spite of traffic between them, immediately brings to mind the familiar canal lock which separates two different water levels, or the air lock which allows movement between areas of different air pressure. We can easily see our analogous social, visual, acoustic, climatic, and technical purposes in the same terms. Each kind of integrity can be maintained only by its particular locks and buffer zones.[7]

If the concept of a "lock" is applied to privacy, it is easy to understand a privacy lock as a transition point between human activities. A privacy lock is actually a zone, which as a buffer will maintain the integrity of public and private areas.

Planting is widely used in the privacy lock or transitional zone between activity areas. With a clear recognition and delineation of the concept of a privacy lock, planting could be used knowledgeably to form such barriers.

Some of these transitional areas are from street to suburban residence, from driveway to residence, from residence to residence, from a parking lot to a public building, from a residential area to a park, from a shopping center to housing units, and from an industrial area to a residential section, at points of mode change—from an auto, or a bus, to foot. Large scale privacy locks for the residential sections of metropolitan areas are created by parks and forest preserves.

Plantings can be used to provide barriers and give privacy in any way and at any scale, as well as to form privacy locks. An individual can be afforded privacy through plantings, or an entire building site may, in fact, be planted in a manner so as to provide privacy.

The degree of privacy is determined by the wishes of the person "inside" and the type of activity which takes place therein. The degree varies from complete blockage of sight and sound to the ephemeral, diaphanous, suggestive veiling, or a "curtain." The amount of privacy required should be determined before planting. The direction, amount, and source of privacy infringement are the prime determinants of the form, size, type, and location of privacy control elements.

Architects are the design professionals who most often face and solve the privacy problem. The materials they use, with some variation, are the same as for other architectural elements. They include wood and wood products, masonry, metal, concrete, plastic, and cloth. The landscape architect may also use, in addition to these materials, earth-forms, water, and plant materials, to form barriers and locks in order to give privacy. Most architectural elements create a solid wall, while plants may form near-solid barriers, but most often act as a pierced barrier, giving privacy in a subtle and sophisticated manner. The amount of privacy plants provide depends upon direction, height, extent, and degree of the barrier required.

When plantings are to be used for privacy, then functional relationships must be considered. Waist-high plants provide partial privacy. Chest-high plants provide privacy while sitting. Plants extending above eye-level provide full privacy. The density of the individual plants and their spacing determines how opaque or translucent the privacy barrier will be. Where full privacy is desired, dense, tall-growing plants must be spaced close together. If a looser, partial privacy is desired, then less dense growing plants may be used. With the wide variety of plants available, the planting designer can use any combination of characteristics of plants to achieve the privacy effect desired. He can use plants alone or combine them with architectural elements.

URBAN PRIVACY - MULTI-DIRECTIONALITY

[7]Serge Chermayeff and Christopher Alexander, *Community and Privacy* (Garden City, 1963), p. 233.

With the yearly increase in population, the need for individual privacy becomes greater; therefore, the utilization of plants as barriers to assure privacy becomes very important. At the same time, with increasing cultural developments, the planting space becomes more scarce. Therefore, plantings must be multifunctional. Certain plants, because of their density and opacity, are able to provide privacy for particular areas and activities. Plantings which are primarily designed for other purposes or functions may be utilized for privacy control as well.

PROGRESSIVE REALIZATION

There are limitless possibilities in the combination of plant forms for progressive realization. The view-step-dichotomy technique discussed earlier is effective to use in combination with progressive realization. The feet or vehicle may be directed and constrained, while the eyes are enticed, limited, or directed.

Progressive realization is probably the least understood and exploited of the functional uses of plant material. However, it is among those design techniques with the most potential for future study and use.

Negative Components

Plants with their forms, delicate textures, and colors are seldom consciously seen, noticed, or appreciated by most people. One of the reasons for this is that the eye is in constant motion, whether the viewer is stationary or moving. Consequently what he envisions as a panorama is, in reality, a sequence of views changing as often and rapidly as he moves. He views whole scenes, and pays little attention to detail unless he is consciously looking for it or has been trained to observe it. Plants in the landscape, not consciously seen or noticed, can be called negative components. The trained planting designer can consciously use plants as negative components to form foreground, background, or frames for activities or views. He can use plants to deliberately block or partially reveal the view beyond, and create a sense of anticipation, wonder, curiosity, and excitement. He can use plants to direct and pull the unconscious viewer through the landscape revealing it, bit by bit.

Concealing and Revealing

A view is usually better if enframed, or seen through an opening. If a view or an object in the landscape is, by design,

slightly rather than fully revealed, the anticipation multiplies the possibilities of perception, and thus expands the scope and richness of the experience. The silhouette or shadow of a pine branch seen through, or projected upon, a translucent panel or screen, is often more interesting than a direct view of the branch itself. The dim outline of an abstract form seen at a distance or in half light is often more exciting than the same form seen fully or in detail. The best view is not always the full view; in fact, the full view is seldom the best view. However, if the full view is worth revealing, then progressive realization is an effective design technique to use.

John Ormsbee Simonds, in his book, **Landscape Architecture,** refers to concealment or revealment and the design technique of progressive realization in the following statement:

A view should be totally revealed in its fullest impact only from that position in the plan where this is most desirable. It is not to be wasted in one first blast, but is to be conserved and displayed with perhaps more refinement, but certainly with no less feeling for suspense and timing than shown by the striptease artist.

He further describes how a view could be progressively revealed:

(1) from a glimpse through loose foliage, (2) to a wider section, (3) to reverse interest, (4) to vista, (5) to object seen against the view, (6) to reverse interest, (7) to objects placed against the view seen through a film of fabric, (8) to concentration in a cave-like recess, (9) to full exuberant sweep.[8]

To effectively create a design using plants for progressive realization, the plants must first be regarded as negative components. The plant and all of its parts must be used so that they are subconsciously perceived by the viewer as a screen, a veil, a foreground, a background, or a frame. It is possible to achieve infinite variation in screening or veiling with plants. A single view from a single vantage point may be screened and veiled to a limited degree. However, multiple views from multiple viewpoints, are better controlled by using a variety of plant types and spacing them to block, veil, and enframe views for progressive realization. Most of the landscape is perceived while moving, either walking or riding; and the speed of movement must be considered in using plants for progressive realization. This technique may call for the removal of some existing plants to enhance a view.

[8]Simonds, pp. 118-119.

APERATURE TYPE

APERATURE SIZE

31

engineering uses
of plants

An entire range of environmental problems are dealt with by the engineering professions. Air pollution control specialists, acoustical engineers, soil conservation specialists, traffic engineers, illuminating engineers, and sanitary and water pollution control engineers, all make significant contributions to solving pressing problems of the landscape and the total environment.

Planting designers have, in the past, used plants intuitively to solve engineering problems. Technical data has now been developed and collected, showing in depth the various abilities of plants to perform these functions. More data is being developed and will continue to be. For example, in highway construction the former emphasis on the use of plant materials was for beautification, with little thought for engineering. The emphasis has now shifted to using plants first for solving engineering problems of noise, glare, barriers, etc., as well as for beautification.

Parts of some plants having characteristics which permit them to solve, or help solve, engineering problems in the environment are:

☐ Fleshy leaves, deadening sound.
☐ Spiny branches, unpleasant to human touch.
☐ Spreading, clinging roots, holding soil.
☐ Pubescence (or hairiness) on leaves, holding dust particles.
☐ Stomata (or openings) in the leaves helping to interchange gases.
☐ Branches moving and vibrating.
☐ Leaves arranged to stop the fall of moisture.
☐ Leaves and branches slowing erosive winds.
☐ Dense foliage blocking light.
☐ Blossoms and foliage providing pleasant odors.
☐ Light foliage filtering light.

Therefore, trees, shrubs, ground cover and turf, may be used to control soil erosion; to control some types of excessive sound; to remove some types of pollutants from the air; to control pedestrian, vehicular, and animal traffic; and to control excessive glare and reflection. When plants are used consciously or unconsciously to perform these functions they are exploited for engineering uses.

The following sections refer to available literature and findings on various engineering uses of plants, providing a source for the environmental planner in solving engineering problems.

EROSION CONTROL

In the course of his cultural development, man has interfered with and disrupted the ecological processes in his environment. When these processes are so disturbed, they are often unbalanced with extremely undesirable effects, one of the most noticeable being soil erosion.

Soil erosion may be defined as wearing away or loss of soil (usually the productive top 7 to 8 inches), by action of wind or water, usually due to lack of proper ground, soil, or earth cover. The degree or severity of soil erosion is determined by the site's exposure to wind and water influences, the climate, the soil character, and the length and degree of slope of the terrain.

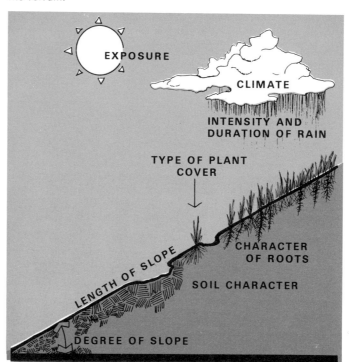

EROSION FACTORS

Wind Erosion

Erosion, on dry, bare earth subject to wind, causes loss of desirable soil, carrying it away as dirt and dust, depositing it as an undesirable nuisance, and creating a safety hazard by reducing visibility. Climatic factors governing erosion caused by wind are wind direction, intensity, and duration. Soil factors are stability of soil crust, size of erodible soil fraction, weight of soil, and amount of soil moisture.

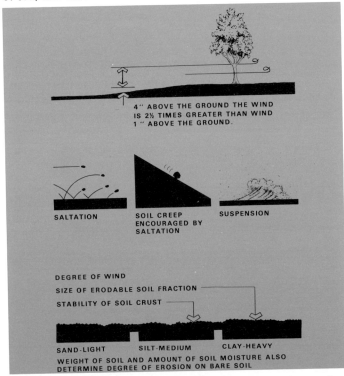

4" ABOVE THE GROUND THE WIND IS 2½ TIMES GREATER THAN WIND 1" ABOVE THE GROUND.

SALTATION

SOIL CREEP ENCOURAGED BY SALTATION

SUSPENSION

DEGREE OF WIND

SIZE OF ERODABLE SOIL FRACTION

STABILITY OF SOIL CRUST

SAND-LIGHT   SILT-MEDIUM   CLAY-HEAVY

WEIGHT OF SOIL AND AMOUNT OF SOIL MOISTURE ALSO DETERMINE DEGREE OF EROSION ON BARE SOIL

When the wind sweeps over exposed, dry earth, the smaller, lighter particles of soil are lifted and held in suspension as dust. Slightly heavier particles, as large as small pebbles, when wind velocity is strong enough, are also lifted. However, the larger particles are too heavy to be carried by the wind, so they are dropped back to the surface, where they bounce and roll, acting as abrasives as long as the wind moves them. This scouring process, called saltation, causes smaller particles to be dislodged and become windborne each time a larger particle falls, thus hastening soil erosion.

Four parts of plants which control wind erosion are dense leaves or needles that create an effective barrier to air movement through the plants; dense branching that controls and slows wind close to the ground; multiple stems and rough bark that decrease wind velocity as it passes through them; and fibrous roots that grow close to the surface and effectively hold surface soil in place.

Plants as windbreaks slow damaging wind in proportion to the heights of the plants used. The area protected by a plant windbreak is twice the height of the windbreak upward, and 18 times the height downwind. The best plants for wind-erosion control are ground covers or those which are densely branched to the ground, and those having a fibrous and shallow root system.

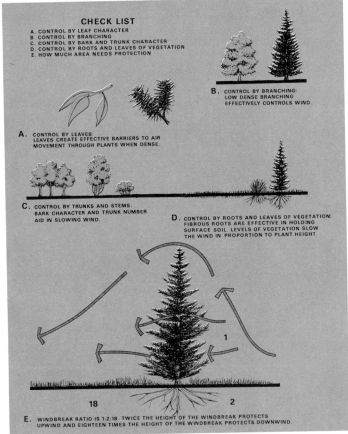

CHECK LIST
A. CONTROL BY LEAF CHARACTER
B. CONTROL BY BRANCHING
C. CONTROL BY BARK AND TRUNK CHARACTER
D. CONTROL BY ROOTS AND LEAVES OF VEGETATION
E. HOW MUCH AREA NEEDS PROTECTION

A. CONTROL BY LEAVES: LEAVES CREATE EFFECTIVE BARRIERS TO AIR MOVEMENT THROUGH PLANTS WHEN DENSE.

B. CONTROL BY BRANCHING: LOW DENSE BRANCHING EFFECTIVELY CONTROLS WIND.

C. CONTROL BY TRUNKS AND STEMS: BARK CHARACTER AND TRUNK NUMBER AID IN SLOWING WIND.

D. CONTROL BY ROOTS AND LEAVES OF VEGETATION: FIBROUS ROOTS ARE EFFECTIVE IN HOLDING SURFACE SOIL. LEVELS OF VEGETATION SLOW THE WIND IN PROPORTION TO PLANT HEIGHT.

18   2

E. WINDBREAK RATIO IS 1:2:18. TWICE THE HEIGHT OF THE WINDBREAK PROTECTS UPWIND AND EIGHTEEN TIMES THE HEIGHT OF THE WINDBREAK PROTECTS DOWNWIND.

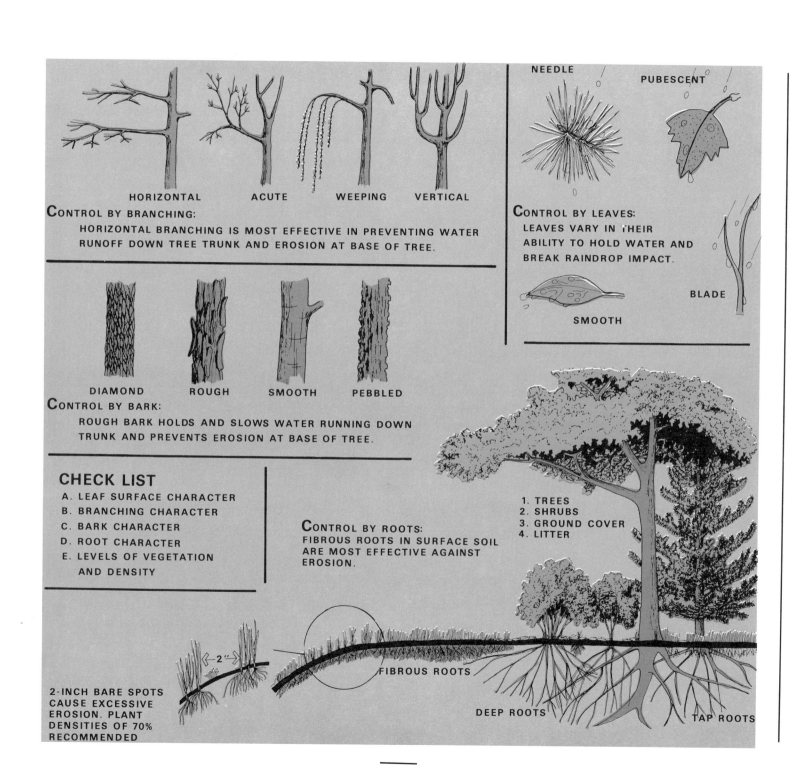

HORIZONTAL   ACUTE   WEEPING   VERTICAL

CONTROL BY BRANCHING:
HORIZONTAL BRANCHING IS MOST EFFECTIVE IN PREVENTING WATER
RUNOFF DOWN TREE TRUNK AND EROSION AT BASE OF TREE.

DIAMOND   ROUGH   SMOOTH   PEBBLED

CONTROL BY BARK:
ROUGH BARK HOLDS AND SLOWS WATER RUNNING DOWN
TRUNK AND PREVENTS EROSION AT BASE OF TREE.

NEEDLE   PUBESCENT

CONTROL BY LEAVES:
LEAVES VARY IN THEIR
ABILITY TO HOLD WATER AND
BREAK RAINDROP IMPACT.

BLADE

SMOOTH

CHECK LIST
A. LEAF SURFACE CHARACTER
B. BRANCHING CHARACTER
C. BARK CHARACTER
D. ROOT CHARACTER
E. LEVELS OF VEGETATION
   AND DENSITY

CONTROL BY ROOTS:
FIBROUS ROOTS IN SURFACE SOIL
ARE MOST EFFECTIVE AGAINST
EROSION.

1. TREES
2. SHRUBS
3. GROUND COVER
4. LITTER

2"

FIBROUS ROOTS

**2-INCH BARE SPOTS
CAUSE EXCESSIVE
EROSION. PLANT
DENSITIES OF 70%
RECOMMENDED**

DEEP ROOTS

TAP ROOTS

Water Erosion

Water is the most common soil eroding agent. It erodes by the impact of raindrops on bare soil, thereby displacing the soil and causing it to mix with the water and to be carried away (splash erosion). As water runs off from saturated soils, it carries loose soil particles with it. Once surface soil is removed and held in suspension by moving water, it acts as a scouring agent, loosening and removing more soil.

Run-off erosion is classified four ways: sheet erosion, rill erosion, gully erosion, and slip erosion. Sheet erosion is the removal of the entire soil layer from an exposed site at once. As erosion continues on an exposed site, softer areas in the surface wash away faster, and small rills, or troughs, carrying water and soil downslope, are formed. As more water and soil flow down the rills, they jam together, become deeper and form gullies, which become deep and expansive if not controlled. Slip erosion is the release of water-saturated, unstable types of soil on steep slopes, sliding downslope as a mass.

Plants can be used to control and prevent water-caused soil erosion in at least three ways. Leaves and branches form canopies or blankets interrupting raindrops, thus reducing splash erosion. Roots form fibrous masses within the soil, holding it in

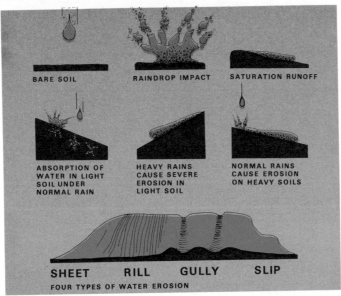

BARE SOIL   RAINDROP IMPACT   SATURATION RUNOFF

ABSORPTION OF WATER IN LIGHT SOIL UNDER NORMAL RAIN   HEAVY RAINS CAUSE SEVERE EROSION IN LIGHT SOIL   NORMAL RAINS CAUSE EROSION ON HEAVY SOILS

SHEET   RILL   GULLY   SLIP

FOUR TYPES OF WATER EROSION

place. Leaves and other dead parts of plants on the soil surface increase the organic material in the soil, loosening it and increasing its water rate absorption.

Splash erosion is controlled at different levels. Rain is first intercepted and held momentarily at a canopy level. Large trees are most effective for this purpose. However, raindrops intercepted at high canopy level regain some force unless they are intercepted again before reaching the soil. The second level at which they are intercepted is at the understory trees or large shrub level. Below either of these two levels, raindrops are intercepted by grasses, ferns, and low shrubs at ground level. The denser the foliage, the more efficient it will be in preventing splash erosion. Deciduous plants are more effective than conifers in preventing splash erosion, because of the spread of their leaf patterns. This is true only when they are in leaf.

Run-off erosion is best controlled by plants having shallow, fibrous roots, which spread throughout the soil. Their secondary roots and root hairs intercept and hold the soil in place. These root systems tend to loosen the soil and add organic matter, which increases the soil's permeability. The plant stems or stalks, particularly grasses, also control run-off by interfering with and intercepting the water as it flows across the ground.

Plants are more effective and attractive than most other paving and slope erosion control devices; therefore, they should be used when grading and changing the natural landforms.

ACOUSTICAL CONTROL

Noise (excessive or unwanted sound) is an increasing problem particularly in urban areas. Acoustical experts call noise invisible pollution. They have warned us that noise has increased to the point of threatening human happiness and health.

A task force on noise control in New York City declared recently that the noise in that city has reached a level that is intense, continuous, and persistent enough to threaten basic community life. Therefore, excessive sound or noise must be decreased or controlled. To control sound, it is necessary to understand what it is, and then how to alleviate or control it.

The day will come when man will have to fight merciless noise as the worst enemy of his health.

—Dr. Robert Koch, 1910.[1]

Noise . . . is one of the chief drawbacks to the enjoyment of modern urban living.

—Dr. Vern O. Knudsen, 1967.[1]

In all probability the noise level will grow not only in urban centers; but with the increasing population and the proliferation of machines, noise will invade the few remaining havens of silence in the world. A century from now, when a man wants to escape to a quiet spot, there may be no place left to go.

—Dr. Leo L. Beranek, 1967.[1]

Properties of Sound

The study of sound takes into consideration its physical and psychological effects. The physical aspect deals with radiation and transmission of sound in the air, while the psychological treats subject response of humans to sound.

In their simplest form, the basic properties of sound are: Sound moves in waves with the highest pitched or highest frequency sound having the shortest wave lengths and the lower pitched or lower frequency sound having progressively longer wave lengths. Sound pitch or frequency is measured in cycles per second. The human ear can detect at the extreme, sounds from approximately 20 to 20,000 cycles per second. Sound may be carried by the wind. The degree of transmission of sound is affected by the density and humidity of the air through which it passes.

Sound generally rises when originating at ground level. Sound, when absorbed, is converted into other forms of energy and, ultimately, into heat. When sound waves strike a surface, the alternating wave pressures against the surface may force it into vibration. Light, flexible panels obviously vibrate more easily and thus absorb more sound than massive, stiff surfaces.

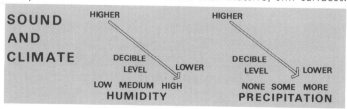

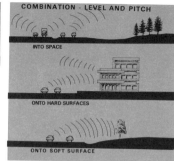

The level or intensity of the sound is measured in decibels (dB). The lowest sound that can be detected by a keen human ear under very quiet conditions is called a decibel (dB). The decibel scale is logarithmic. The actual sound pressure on the ear, increases 10 times with each 10 decibel increase. Thus a level of 100 decibels is really 10 to the 10th power—or 10 billion times as intense a pressure as 1 decibel.

However, for each 10 percent increase in decibels, the hearer experiences the sound as doubling in intensity. When the sound goes up from a normal conversational level of 50 dB to 100 dB (the sound of a loud outboard motor) the ear suffers a 100,000-fold increase in pressure, and hears the sound 32 times louder.

Thus, a whisper at 5 feet is 30 decibels and a jet taking off 200 feet away makes a 120 decibel noise indicating that the jet is 512 times louder than the whisper. Further reducing the energy of a sound to 10 percent of its initial value, corresponding to a 10 dB reduction, yields a sound that seems only half as loud as the initial one.[2]

Sound level and pitch are experienced in combination. Generally lower pitched sounds are not heard at lower sound levels; however, if the sound level is increased enough, sound may be felt rather than heard.

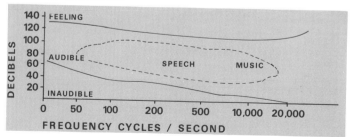

[1]*Conservation Foundation Newsletter* (December 29, 1967), p. 1.
[2]See the Unpublished manuscript (Connecticut Agricultural Experiment Station, 1970) by Donald Aylor, "Can Plants Filter Noise from our Environment?" p. 1.

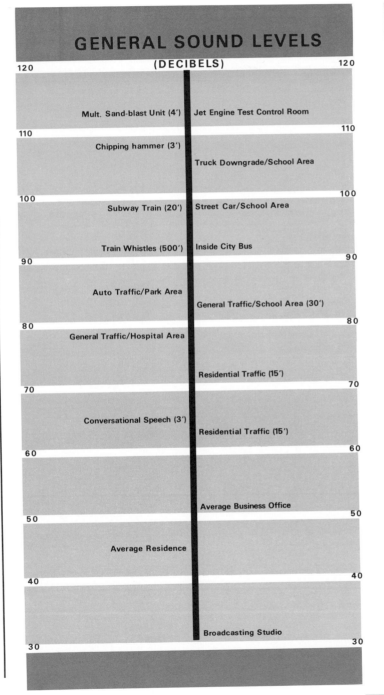

GENERAL SOUND LEVELS
(DECIBELS)

120	120
Mult. Sand-blast Unit (4')	Jet Engine Test Control Room
110	110
Chipping hammer (3')	
	Truck Downgrade/School Area
100	100
Subway Train (20')	Street Car/School Area
Train Whistles (500')	Inside City Bus
90	90
Auto Traffic/Park Area	
	General Traffic/School Area (30')
80	80
General Traffic/Hospital Area	
	Residential Traffic (15')
70	70
Conversational Speech (3')	
	Residential Traffic (15')
60	60
	Average Business Office
50	50
Average Residence	
40	40
	Broadcasting Studio
30	30

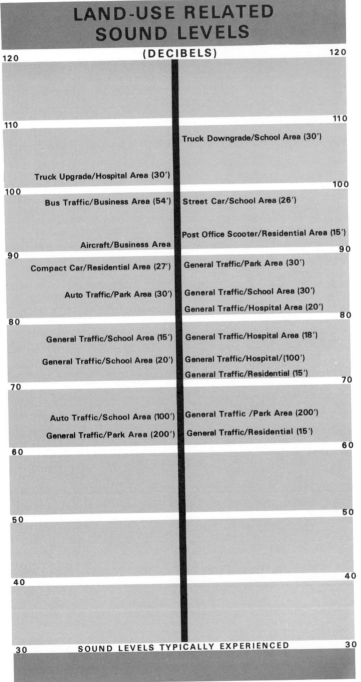

LAND-USE RELATED SOUND LEVELS
(DECIBELS)

120	120
110	110
	Truck Downgrade/School Area (30')
Truck Upgrade/Hospital Area (30')	
100	100
Bus Traffic/Business Area (54')	Street Car/School Area (26')
	Post Office Scooter/Residential Area (15')
Aircraft/Business Area	
90	90
Compact Car/Residential Area (27')	General Traffic/Park Area (30')
Auto Traffic/Park Area (30')	General Traffic/School Area (30')
	General Traffic/Hospital Area (20')
80	80
General Traffic/School Area (15')	General Traffic/Hospital Area (18')
General Traffic/School Area (20')	General Traffic/Hospital/(100')
	General Traffic/Residential (15')
70	70
Auto Traffic/School Area (100')	General Traffic /Park Area (200')
General Traffic/Park Area (200')	General Traffic/Residential (15')
60	60
50	50
40	40
30	30

SOUND LEVELS TYPICALLY EXPERIENCED

Noise

Methods of categorizing noises vary from the type of noise created to the sources of the created noise. The source may be designated as to its extent or its specific cause, or the type of activity which gives rise to certain classes of noise. Noise is undesired sound, and does not actually exist apart from the experience of a receiver whose central nervous system reacts to a particular adverse sound. There are three elements of concern in any noise problem—sound, transmission paths, and receiver. Generally the receiver is understood to be a human (or other animal), although it could also be a piece of mechanical equipment sensitive to sound vibrations.

Noise may come from a variety of sources. It may originate from linear sources such as highways. "Spot" noises may originate from a single source where a specific type of activity exists, such as a service station or a swimming pool. Noise may also originate from an area of activity, such as a manufacturing plant or an airport.

Before an attempt is made to control noise, all noise sources should be identified. Most noises may be categorized according to their associative emanation, i.e., their source of origin. There are distinctive noises generated in areas of transportation, recreation, industry, commerce, or in residential areas:

☐ Examples of transportation noises are the sounds of horns, engines, tire squeal, and sirens, caused by cars, trucks, trains, airplanes, ships, helicopters, motorcycles, police cars, fire engines, or ambulances.

☐ Some noises associated with recreation may include those from swimming pools, playgrounds, ballfields, or they may be caused by motorboats, snowmobiles, or model airplanes.

☐ Noises associated with commercial areas may include those from shopping centers, manufacturing plants, and warehouses.

☐ Distinctive noises in residential areas include those generated by lawnmowers, air-conditioning equipment, excessively loud human voices, and radios.

How then, can such noise or sound be controlled? Sound energy from a source usually spreads out and never returns to the source. Sound will be dissipated in transmission. Sound waves can be absorbed, reflected, deflected, or refracted when they meet a barrier or change of medium. Sound can be partially diminished by multiple reflection to produce reverberant sound.

Attenuation of Sound

Outdoor sounds are usually attenuated or reduced in intensity before reaching the receiver. Basically, attenuation is of two types. The first of these is normal attenuation due to distance. The second is excess attenuation resulting from the introduction of elements or barriers between the sound source and the receiver. Excess attenuation may be accomplished by introducing any number and type of elements between the sound source and the receiver.

NORMAL ATTENUATION   In discussing attenuation or reduction of sound due to distance, John E. Moore, in his book, **Design for Noise Reduction,** explains how normal attenuation is accomplished. As the sound travels over a distance it is partially absorbed by the air and partially absorbed by the ground. He says:

The reduction in sound level due to the distance in the case of a point of sound is shown in the . . . chart and is applicable at all frequencies. It will be seen that each time the distance from the source is doubled, there is a reduction of 6 dB. In the case of multiple sound sources, the rate of reduction in over-all sound level will be less and will depend on a number of factors. To take a typical example, however, in the case of a stream of vehicles on a busy main road, the reduction in sound level due to distance is doubled.[3]

EXCESS ATTENUATION   Other factors contributing to the reduction of sound or excess attenuation are climatic conditions, and the introduction of elements between the sound source and the receiver. Climatic conditions have an affect on sound attenuation. Moore indicates that the attenuation of sound as it travels may be modified and the rate of attenuation changed by wind and temperature. In addition, Beranek says in his book, **Noise Reduction:**

This excess attenuation of sound propagated along the ground is profoundly affected by the presence of temperature and wind gradients. Attenuation measured upwind may exceed those measured downwind by as much as 25 to 30 decibels.[4]

[3]John E. Moore, *Design for Noise Reduction* (London, 1966), p. 133.
[4]Leo L. Beranek, *Noise Reduction* (New York, 1960), p. 197.

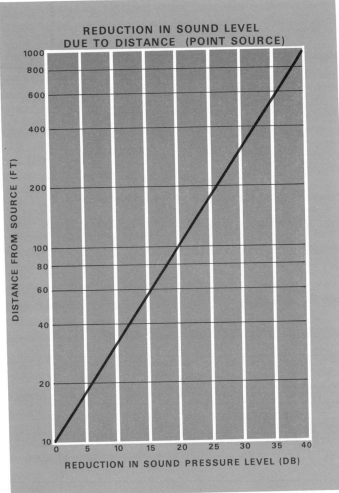

**REDUCTION IN SOUND LEVEL
DUE TO DISTANCE (POINT SOURCE)**

Y-axis: DISTANCE FROM SOURCE (FT)
X-axis: REDUCTION IN SOUND PRESSURE LEVEL (DB)

Donald Aylor, of the Connecticut Agricultural Experiment Station in New Haven, states that:

Weather also affects sound. Wind and temperature differences above the ground can work together to force sound up, creating a sound shadow or wind and temperature profiles can channel overhead sound back to the ground. We hear sounds farther downwind than upwind from a source, and better morning and evening than at midday.[5]

Elements introduced between the sound source and the receiver reduce sound by absorption, deflection, reflection, and defraction of sound waves.

[5]Aylor, p. 3.
[6]Beranek, *Noise Reduction*, p. 32.

Absorption takes place when an element receives the sound waves and entraps or absorbs them, converting the sound into other energy forms and, ultimately, heat.

. . . Most manufactured materials depend largely on their porosity for their sound absorptivity. Many materials, such as mineral wools, pads, and blankets have a multitude of small, deeply penetrating inter-communicating pores. The sound waves can readily propagate themselves into these interstices where a portion of the sound energy is converted into heat by frictional and viscous resistance within the pores and by vibration of the small fibers of the material. If the material is sufficiently porous, and of appropriate thickness, as much as 95 percent of the energy of an incident sound wave may be absorbed in this manner.

When sound waves strike a panel, the alternating pressure of these waves against the panel may force it into vibration. The resulting flexural vibrations use up a certain amount of the incident sound energy by converting it into heat. If the panel is massive and stiff, the amount of acoustical energy converted into mechanical vibrations of the panel is exceedingly small; on the other hand, if the panel is light and flexible, the amount of energy absorbed may be very large, especially at low frequencies.[6]

Deflection is accomplished by introducing an element which causes the noise to be bounced away from a recipient into an area or direction less offensive to the hearer.

Reflection causes the sound to be reflected toward its source, thus shielding the receptor from offense.

Refraction occurs when acoustical energy is dissipated, diffused, or dispersed by striking a rough surface. Sound is also disbersed by turbulence and gusty winds; and sound shadows may be produced upwind of noise sources.

Masking while not actually a form of attenuation, occurs when "white" sound is introduced to override unpleasant or undesirable noise. For example piped-in music in offices is a form of masking unpleasant or undesirable sound.

Plants As Attenuators

Many common acoustical control elements have been well-researched and documented as to their ability to attenuate sound. Plant materials as natural elements, however, have not been researched adequately to provide the necessary technical information in regard to their efficacy or efficiency. Few comprehensive, quantitative studies have been undertaken to show the relative effectiveness of plants in controlling sound. However, throughout the years there have been three basic sources of information concerning the effectiveness of plants in attenuation of excess noise in the out-of-doors. These are a study by Carl F. Eyring, **Jungle Acoustics,** conducted in Panama in 1945 and 1946;[7] a study by Francis M. Weiner and David N. Keast, **Sound Propagation over Terrain,**[8] conducted in 1954 through 1958; and a study by Dr. T. F. W. Embleton, **Sound Propagation in Homogeneous, Deciduous and Evergreen Woods;** 1962.[9]

Other studies have been conducted in recent years, and statements concerning the effectiveness of plants in acoustical control have come from a variety of sources. Some information is available to guide in the use of plants to control sound levels.

Basically, the effectiveness of plants to control sound levels is determined by the sound—its type, decibel level, intensity and origin; the planting—type, height, density, and location; and the climatic factors—wind direction and velocity, temperature, and humidity.

Plants are more effective in screening sounds at some frequencies than at others. Human ears are more sensitive to some sound levels than others, particularly the higher frequencies. Plants, while not absolutely effective in the screening of all sounds, do seem to screen out sound levels sensitive to human ears. Plants do this by modifying climatic conditions, and by absorption, deflection, refraction, and reflection of noise.

PLANTS MODIFY LOCAL CLIMATE
Plants exert some control over local climates and thus attenuate sound. Sound is also dispersed by turbulence and gusty winds. Sound shadows may be produced upwind of noise sources even with gentle, steady winds. If the air close to the ground is moving slowly, sound waves are reflected upwards, and there may be a zone of quiet for 200 or 2,000 feet upwind. However, these effects cannot always be depended upon.

The ability of vegetation to control climate and thus reduce sound transmission is discussed by Weiner and Keast. They say:

It is clear that results obtained for propagation of sound over open level terrain will not apply where the transmission path is predominantly in a woods. This is true because in dense woods the wind velocity and vertical wind gradients are very much smaller for given wind velocity above the tree tops than the wind velocity and vertical wind gradients over open level ground. Furthermore, the air temperature in dense woods is very nearly uniform during most of the day and night, and the large diurnal lapse rates and nocturnal inversions characteristic of open terrain are absent. Because of absorption by the ground and cover and the foliage of the trees on the one hand, and multiple scattering by tree trunks and limbs on the other hand, the sound pressure level in forests diminishes quite rapidly with distance from the source . . . . The relative importance of scattering versus absorption will be different, depending on the ratio of scatterers to absorbers.[10]

PLANTS ABSORB SOUND
The vibrations of sound waves are absorbed by leaves, branches, and twigs of trees. As mentioned previously, light, flexible, porous panels are best for absorption of sound; therefore, it follows that the most effective plant for absorbing unwanted noise is one which has many, thick, fleshy leaves with thin petioles allowing for a high degree of flexibility and vibration.

In discussing the acoustical properties of plants in their paper on **The Importance of Green Areas in Urban Planning,** Dr. Wilfrid Bach and Dr. Edward Mathews refer to the work of William Siekman (Manager of the Riverbank Acoustical Laboratories in Geneva, Ill.), explaining that in spite of the weak-

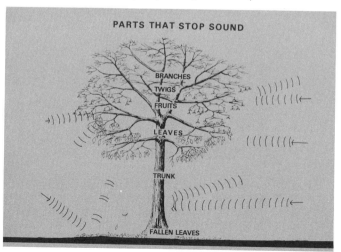

PARTS THAT STOP SOUND

[7]Carl F. Eyring, "Jungle Acoustics," *Journal of the Acoustical Society of America* (October 1946), p. 731.

[8]Francis M. Weiner and David N. Keast, "Sound Propagation over Terrain," *Journal of the Acoustical Society of America* (June 1959), p. 732.

[9]T. F. W. Embleton, "Sound Propagation in Homogenous, Deciduous and Evergreen Woods," *Journal of the Acoustical Society of America* (August 1963), p. 1121.

[10]Weiner and Keast, p. 734.

ness of their sound absorption, trees are effective in scattering or diffusing sound, and thereby add to the effectiveness of grass in absorbing sounds over a wider range of incidence.[11]

An article by Embleton, refers to his studies of tree branches as oscillators for absorbing sound. He indicated that the normal resonant frequencies in wood are approximately 400 to 500 cycles per sound. He mentions laboratory studies indicating that:

. . . it was quickly shown that it was the branch itself and not the twigs, needles, or leaves, that were capable of acoustic response in this frequency range. All the branches had one well-defined resonance lying between about 275 and 450 cycles per second. Because of this, then, plant parts act as vibrators or resonators or oscillators absorbing and deadening excessive noise.[12]

Subsequent correspondence between Embleton and M. R. Guthrie of Louisville, Ky., indicates new information in this regard. Embleton wrote:

Further thoughts on the problem cause me to think now that trees behave mainly as non-resonant scatterers with very little absorption. The measured energy density at any distance from a source is approximately the undisturbed sound field, less energy scattered into other directions by trees in front of the observation point, plus energy scattered to the observation point by trees behind it and on either side. These two factors are different functions of frequency and geometry of the situation. Usually the former predominates—leading to a net reduction of energy and hence a measured excess attenuation due to the trees.

If this is correct, most species of trees would behave acoustically in the same way—the experimental results on the four species support this. Bigger plant species would presumably scatter more energy at lower frequencies, and smaller plants less energy with the maximum scattering being at higher frequencies—but I have no experimental evidence on this point.[13]

Investigation of the acoustical properties of turf at the Riverbank Acoustical Laboratory in Geneva, Ill., was reported in personal correspondence by Siekman:

We decided to investigate the acoustical properties of grass, since it is a part of our "natural" environment, and were pleased to discover its very large (sound) absorption (ability). The absorption coefficient is the fraction of incident sound which is totally absorbed at each single reflection. The

coefficient for merion blue-grass and a typical heavy carpet on a felt pad are as follows:

Frequency, cps	125	250	500	1,000	2,000	4,000
Grass	0.11	0.26	0.50	0.69	0.92	0.99
Carpet & Pad	.08	.24	.57	.69	.71	.73

The favorable, somewhat superior performance of grass is impressive.[14]

The ability of grass to absorb sound is also shown in a chart from Moore's book, **Design for Noise Reduction.**

REDUCTION IN SOUND LEVEL DUE TO ABSORPTION OVER GRASS						
FREQUENCY C/S	125	250	500	1000	2000	4000
Reduction, DB per 100 feet, over rough grass	0.5	1.5	3.0	2.5	1.0	1.0

PLANTS DEFLECT AND REFRACT SOUND The foliage of trees, because of their flexibility and softness, absorb sound; the trunks and heavier branches deflect sound. As has been pointed out, scattering and absorbing sound waves by plants, grass, and ground cover, reduces the sound level. Aylor makes the following statement:

The information already available allows us to guess how vegetation will attenuate sound. Assuming that forests, on the average, will attenuate a 1,000 cps sound by 7 dB per 100 feet, the following example indicates the value of this reduction. We know that sound energy will be reduced as the distance from the source increases. The energy of a sound measured at 25 feet will be reduced by 14 dB at 125 feet. However, if 100 feet of forest lies between the source and observer the reduction will be 21 dB. To obtain the same reduction by distance alone, one would have to be 250 feet from the source. Therefore, the substitution of vegetation for distance as a sound screen seems to be a promising way of restoring some quiet to our environment.[15]

In previously cited studies it was found that plants reduced unwanted noise by 7 decibels per 100-foot width of planting (Embleton). It has been stated that grass or ground cover on the sides of a depressed expressway embankment doubles the degree of sound reduction effected by paving on the same bank. A frequently quoted statistic from Knudsen states that a cypress hedge 2 feet thick deadens sound by 4 decibels.[16]

[11]Wilfrid Bach and Edward Mathews, "The Importance of Green Acres in Urban Planning," Paper prepared for Bioclimatology and Environmental Health Workshop, Public Health Service, U.S. Department of Health, Education, and Welfare, Cincinnati, July 14-16, 1969, p. 9.

[12]Embleton, p. 1122.

[13]Letter from T. F. W. Embleton to M. R. Guthrie, July 30, 1970.

[14]Letter from William Seikman to author, May 5, 1969.

[15]Aylor, p. 2.

[16]Vern O. Knudsen and Cyril M. Harris, *Acoustical Designing in Architecture* (New York, 1950). p. 137.

To point up the varying ability of plants to lessen sound of different frequencies, sound of 4,000 cycles per second is reduced 5 decibels per 100 feet by dense foliage, while sound of 1,000 cycles per second is reduced by 2 decibels per 100 feet.

The accompanying chart from the firm of Bolt, Beranek & Newman, is indicative of the average excess attenuation in

EXCESS ATTENUATION IN OCTAVE BAND FOR SOUND PROPAGATION IN TREE AREAS IN DB PER 100 FT

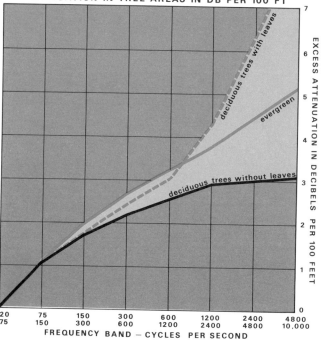

octave bands for sound propagation in tree areas in decibels per 100 feet. According to Moore:

The effectiveness of trees and shrubs as acoustic screens is unpredictable for a number of reasons. The density of foliage varies considerably according to the type of tree and near ground level may be negligible.

Trees which shed their leaves will be ineffective during the winter months. Wind gradients caused by the obstruction of planting may offset the advantage of screening when air movement is in the direction of the listener.

Even where foliage is dense, the attenuation of sound appears to be small. The following figure indicates a negligible atten-

uation of middle and low frequencies unless the belt of trees is very deep. The attenuation of high frequencies may, however, account for the general impression that planting reduces the apparent loudness of sounds in some situations.[17]

ATTENUATION OF SOUND DUE TO DENSE FOLIAGE						
FREQUENCY C/S	125	250	500	1000	2000	4000
Reduction, DB, per 100 ft	0.8	1.5	1.8	2.0	3.0	5.0

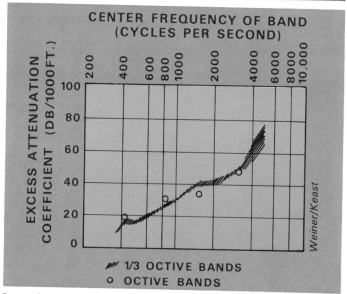

Beranek, in his book, **Noise Reduction,** gives an example of a jet-engine test stand surrounded by dense woods 1,000 feet in depth. He then asks the question: *"What is the excess attenuation provided by the woods in the 300 to 600-cps band?"*[18] A chart by Weiner and Keast shows the effectiveness of plants in controlling sound. Embleton in his previously mentioned article has two charts showing the relative effectiveness of cedar, pine, spruce, and deciduous trees in controlling sound and a composite chart showing the effectiveness of all types of vegetation in controlling sound.

The latest study of the effectiveness of plants in reducing noise has been jointly conducted by the School of Engineering at the University of Nebraska and The Rocky Mountain Forest and Range Experiment Station. It was made possible by a grant from the U.S. Forest Service. In this study Prof.

[17]Moore, *Design for Noise Reduction* p. 104.
[18]Beranek, *Noise Reduction,* p. 204.

David I. Cook and Dr. David F. van Haverbeke have found that tree species do not differ greatly in their ability to reduce traffic noise levels, but evergreen varieties are best when year-round screening is desired. They have indicated that the sound barrier effect is greater with tall trees and with wide belts of trees, because sound is diffused and absorbed over a larger area. They have, understandably, found that the softness or hardness of the surface over which sound travels also greatly affects noise levels. Soft surfaces, such as lawns with tree or shrub borders, absorb sound, while hard surfaces, such as highways and parking lots, reflect and may even amplify sound. Other findings of their studies were:

Distances of 75 feet or more should be available for planting between the noise sources and the area to be protected. Dense barriers formed by planting several rows of trees closely together are most effective. Noise screens should be placed as close as possible to the noise sources, consistent with safety.[19]

[19]David I. Cook and David F. Van Haverbeke, "Trees and Shrubs for Noise Abatement," Paper prepared for Trees and Forests in an Urbanizing Environment Symposium, University of Massachusetts, 1970, p. 4.

[20]Burton H. Sexton, "Traffic Noise," *Traffic Quarterly* (July 1969), p. 436.

[21]Wilbur H. Simonson, "Abatement of Highway Noise with Special Reference to Roadside Planting," *Highway Research Bulletin,* no. 110 (1955).

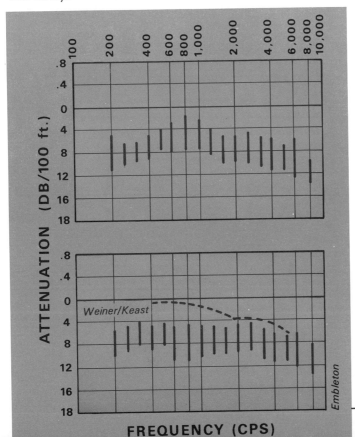

What then, is the type of planting most effective in controlling unwanted noise? What is the thickness or depth required in noise control planting? Burton H. Sexton, in his article in the **Traffic Quarterly,** states:

Almost all buffer plantings offer some noise reduction. However, the effectiveness will not always increase with the extensiveness of the growth. Buffer plantings ranging from 20 to 50 feet in depth, depending upon the height and density, have produced satisfactory results. Even where the noise reduction may not be considered significant, the effects of the plantings together with their esthetic value will produce a positive influence.[20]

For the most effective screening of highway noise, the planting width should be from 25 to 35 feet. For maximum effectiveness a planting consists of both trees and shrubs, since the shrubs are not high enough nor the trees branched low enough to the ground. Border plantings, to control noise, should be lower toward the source and higher toward the hearer. This directs the unwanted noise upward, away from the hearer.

For year-round effectiveness, a narrow planting requires a greater proportion of evergreens than does a wide planting. The proportion of evergreens may be reduced, however, if a "buffer" is needed in warm weather. Deciduous trees are relatively ineffective in winter. Densely growing plants are best for sound control and width of planting is a decisive factor. When small plants are used as buffer plantings several years of growth are required to effectively control noise. Immediate results cannot be expected.

The Highway Research Board has conducted many highway design and roadside development studies to alleviate traffic noises. A Special Task Committee on Roadside Design to Reduce Traffic Noise, Dust and Fumes, chaired by Wilbur Simonson, who at the time was the chief of the Roadside Section of the Bureau of Public Roads, suggested optimum planting of cross sections for sound control along highways, which were either depressed, raised, or on grade. This committee also suggested possible configurations of plantings on top of retaining walls and buffer planting on roadsides, as well as on abutting property, to most effectively control noise.[21]

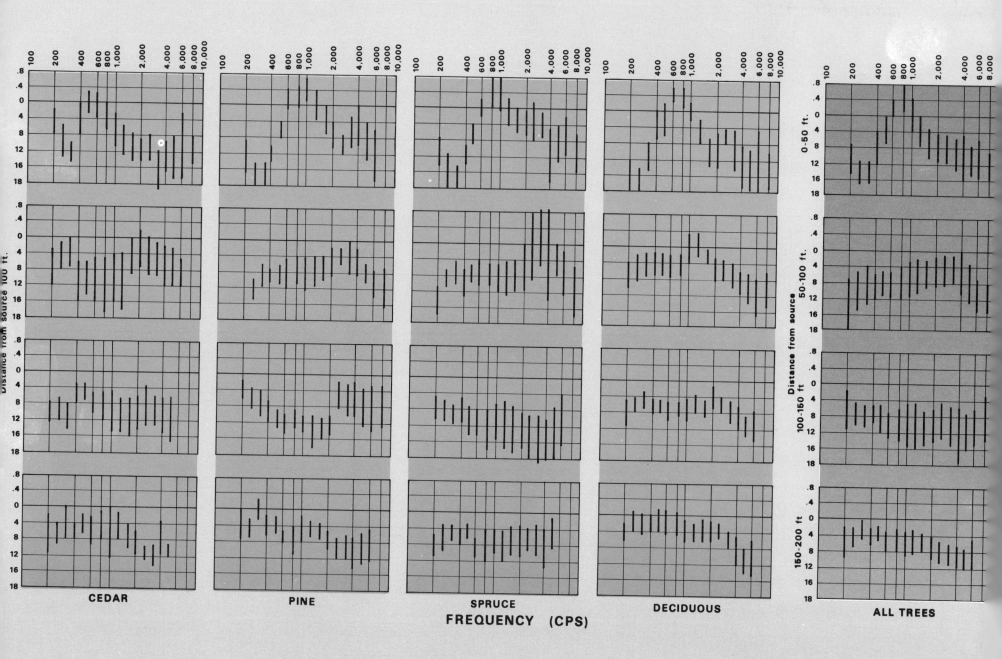

FREQUENCY (CPS)

CEDAR   PINE   SPRUCE   DECIDUOUS   ALL TREES

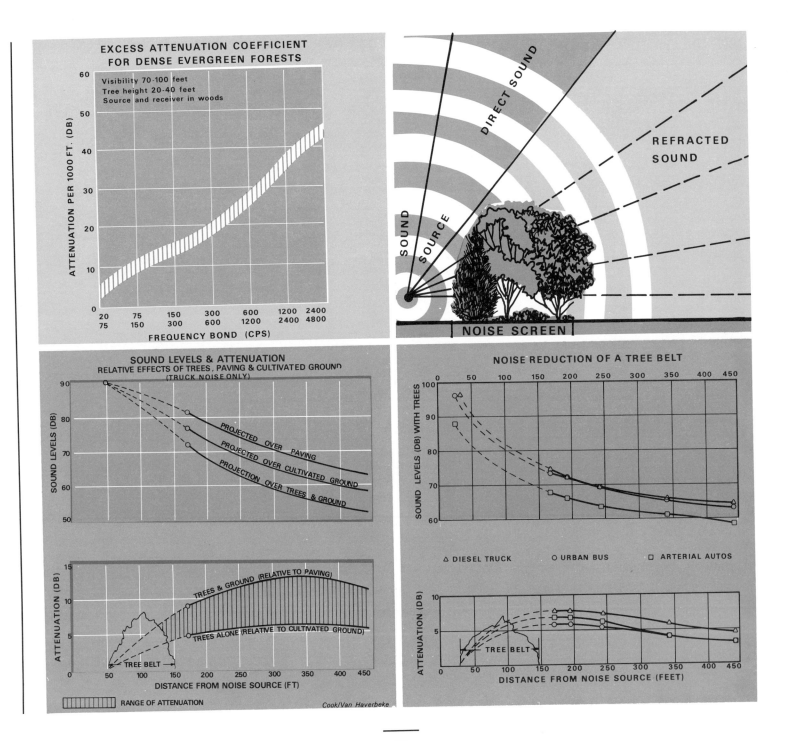

EXCESS ATTENUATION COEFFICIENT
FOR DENSE EVERGREEN FORESTS

Visibility 70-100 feet
Tree height 20-40 feet
Source and receiver in woods

ATTENUATION PER 1000 FT. (DB)

FREQUENCY BOND (CPS)

DIRECT SOUND

REFRACTED SOUND

SOUND SOURCE

NOISE SCREEN

SOUND LEVELS & ATTENUATION
RELATIVE EFFECTS OF TREES, PAVING & CULTIVATED GROUND
(TRUCK NOISE ONLY)

SOUND LEVELS (DB)

PROJECTED OVER PAVING
PROJECTED OVER CULTIVATED GROUND
PROJECTION OVER TREES & GROUND

ATTENUATION (DB)

TREES & GROUND (RELATIVE TO PAVING)
TREES ALONE (RELATIVE TO CULTIVATED GROUND)

TREE BELT

DISTANCE FROM NOISE SOURCE (FT)

||||| RANGE OF ATTENUATION

Cook/Van Haverbeke

NOISE REDUCTION OF A TREE BELT

SOUND LEVELS (DB) WITH TREES

△ DIESEL TRUCK   ○ URBAN BUS   □ ARTERIAL AUTOS

ATTENUATION (DB)

TREE BELT

DISTANCE FROM NOISE SOURCE (FEET)

NOISE ZONE

DEPRESSED SECTION

NOISE ZONE

RAISED SECTION

NOISE ZONE

LEVEL SECTION

Residence, Apartment or Hotel

PLANTINGS ABOVE WALL BUFFER NOISE

RETAINING WALL

R.O.W. LINE

R.O.W. LINE

Residence, Apartment or Hotel

SET BACK

R.O.W. LINE

DEPRESSED HIGHWAYS WITH BUFFER PLANTINGS CONTROL NOISE

SET BACK

R.O.W. LINE

Plants With Other Elements

Plants absorb sound waves in the vibration of leaves and branches. They break up waves and change their direction and they divert wind which carries sound. Plants do this alone or in conjunction with earth forms and architectural structures. Sexton mentioned in his article on traffic noise from the **Traffic Quarterly,** that:

Where rights-of-way are limited, a combination of wall (masonry, barrier, or embankment) and planting can be effective. A typical installation consists of a 5' masonry wall with a dense evergreen hedge maintained at a desired height according to the noise source encountered. An additional advantage can be gained by planting the wall with ivy or other vines, to further increase the effectiveness of the barrier. Such walls are of the dense masonry type and not fencing or other low density type materials.[22]

Peter Kryopoulos, also in an article in the **Traffic Quarterly,** said:

In connection with parkway planning it is well to point out that sound radiates from the source and may be reflected. Depressed highways, therefore, reflect the bulk of traffic noise upwards especially if secondary reflection is avoided by planting on the slopes. Planting along highways, even if not depressed, is very effective in suppressing the noise transmission to adjoining areas.[23]

From an article in **American Highways,** the following quote is taken:

Other preliminary studies have indicated that if the surface of barrier slopes facing the source of noise is absorptive, such as a grassy turf, dense vines, or other planting, the over-all noise reduction may amount to as much as 8 or 10 decibles. Hedges and trees with dense foliage act as sound absorbers and deadeners. Effectiveness of planting increases with the extent (thickness, height, and density) of growth.[24]

Knudsen, has said in personal correspondence:

My own subjective observations convince me that planting of suitable ground covers and dense shrubs and hedges are effective in reducing freeway noise, especially when the freeway has been depressed as much as 15 to 20 feet. A dense ground cover then persists as a sound absorption turf, even in the winter seasons, make a substantial contribution to the reduction of noise from freeways.[25]

[22]Sexton, p. 438.
[23]Peter Kryopoulos, "Traffic Noise," *Traffic Quarterly* (January 1948), p. 31-43.
[24]American Association of State Highway Officials, "Highway Noise Reduced Through Border Planting," American Highways, v. 32 (July 1953), p. 10.
[25]Letter from Vern O. Knudsen to author, August 9, 1967.
[26]Sexton, p. 439.

Therefore, planting, when combined with earth forms or other architectural structures, can be increasingly more effective than the use of plants alone for acoustical control.

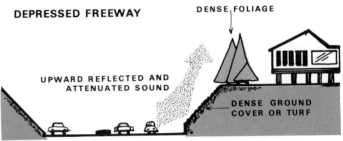

Psychological Effects

Plants absorb, deflect, refract, or reflect sound. In addition to the actual excess attenuation which plants perform, they reduce sound in other ways. Sexton, writing in the July 1969 issue of **Traffic Quarterly,** makes the following statement concerning landscaping in traffic noise control:

The buffer planting of rights-of-way as a noise control feature without the use of masonry barrier is not entirely dependent upon the width of the buffer. However, the psychological advantages cannot be ignored. The presence of a hedge alone will produce psychological results of considerable magnitude whereas the actual noise reduction will be only 2 or 3 decibels. In an actual case study the effect of a five-foot holly hedge which produced a noise reduction of some 2 dB's had a considerable psychological advantage.[26]

Plants Mask Undesirable Sound

When noise levels cannot be reduced to an acceptable point, it is useful to mask them by adding desirable or random sounds—the play of water, music, the rustle of leaves, or even "static" or "white" noises.

Plants, in addition to controlling sounds, in a sense make their own, and assist the wind in masking some offensive noises. The wind moving through pine needles, the rustle of oak leaves, either on the trees or on the ground, the sound of quaking aspen leaves, all constitute pleasant sounds which lessen the hearer's awareness of offensive noises.

Plants attract animals and birds which contribute diversionary sounds. Squirrels, chipmunks, and birds are attracted to trees

SOUND AND PLANTS

PARTS THAT MAKE SOUND

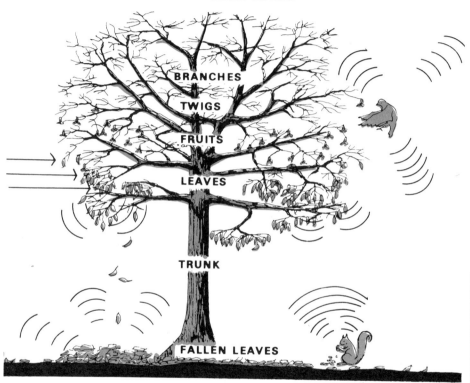

and shrubs. The sounds they make assist in masking offensive or unwanted noises.

An excerpt from a summary of a research project by Stanley Raymond Margules in the Department of Landscape Architecture at the University of California at Davis, contains some significant information concerning masking noises made by plants or birds attracted by plants.

Noises created by breeze are transient and should not be evaluated as having any significance in a design assessment. However, it is necessary to know that the noise produced by breezes in foliage types varies considerably. Two useful plants for producing acceptable foliage noises are bamboo and casurina, which due to different leaf characteristics produce considerable noise levels from slight breezes through the foliage. Casurina, with long pendulous needles like false leaves, *produces a strong whistling noise, while bamboo, from similar breezes, produces a noise from friction between its flat paper leaves.*

Bird calls can be both acceptable and unacceptable noise sources. Often the strong, striking calls of the larger birds are objectionable, but most species for which it is possible to create an attractive environment in a domestic landscape, produce acceptable mixed noises. Birds are also transients; however, if the arbor is well designed, it is possible to establish reasonable stability in the population which will produce continually some masking noise in the landscape.[27]

Further quantitative studies are necessary and undoubtedly will be undertaken to demonstrate clearly the relative effectiveness of plants in performing acoustical control in the exterior environment.

[27]Unpublished Master's thesis (University of California-Davis, 1956) by Stanley Raymond Margules, "The Propagation of Noise in the Landscape Environment," 1956, p. 4.

ATMOSPHERIC PURIFICATION

At a time when there is much talk about air pollution and concern for our air supply, it appears that one of the greatest sources of natural atmospheric purification is being overlooked. It is appropriate to point out that plants condition and cleanse our air. Some of the ways which plants act in doing this are similar to those of commercial interior air-conditioners which heat, cool, humidify, dehumidify, clean, and circulate air. Plants control temperature, air flow, and moisture content. Their efficiency in this is demonstrated in a later section on climate control.

For the purpose of this discussion, however, we are concerned with air cleansing as an engineering function of plant materials. This includes the use of plants for abating gaseous, particulate, and odoriferous air pollution.

Oxygen Carbon Dioxide Cycle

Plants cleanse the air by the process of photosynthesis: in the presence of sunlight carbon dioxide is removed from the air and oxygen is returned to it. Oxygen is vital to the survival of all animals, including man, and carbon dioxide is vital to plant life. This process and interrelationship is explained by Dr. Lamont C. Cole, as follows:

. . . oxygen is an abundant element and actually accounts for about half of the total mass of known terrestrial matter. However, it is a highly reactive element and is almost never found in uncombined form except in the atmosphere or dissolved in bodies of water. In both cases green plants are responsible for the presence of free oxygen. Plants take in carbon dioxide and water and use the energy of sunlight to derive the chemical reaction known as photosynthesis, which produces organic compounds and releases molecular oxygen to the environment as a by-product. . . .[28]

Pollution Control

Plants control air-polluting gasses through oxygenation and dilution.

OXYGENATION The introduction of excess oxygen into the atmosphere is oxygenation. The minimum ratio of air contamination acceptable to man is one part of polluted air to 3,000 parts of relatively pure air. Along many highways the ratio may be as low as 1:1,000. A one-half-mile-wide green-belt, planted on either side of freeways and expressways, would readjust the air balance.

[28]Lamont C. Cole, "Are We Running Out of Oxygen?" *Catalyst for Environmental Quality* (Spring 1970) p. 2.

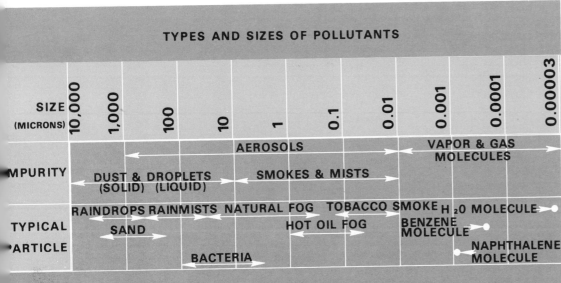

TYPES AND SIZES OF POLLUTANTS

SIZE (MICRONS)	10,000	1,000	100	10	1	0.1	0.01	0.001	0.0001	0.00003
IMPURITY			AEROSOLS				VAPOR & GAS MOLECULES			
	DUST & DROPLETS (SOLID) (LIQUID)		SMOKES & MISTS							
TYPICAL PARTICLE	RAINDROPS RAINMISTS		NATURAL FOG	TOBACCO SMOKE		H₂0 MOLECULE				
	SAND			HOT OIL FOG		BENZENE MOLECULE				
			BACTERIA					NAPHTHALENE MOLECULE		

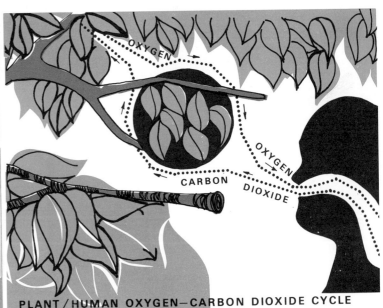

PLANT / HUMAN OXYGEN—CARBON DIOXIDE CYCLE

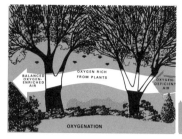

DILUTION The dilution of air is mixing fresh, or "clean" air, with polluted air. Mechanical air conditioners force fresh air into an area containing stale, impure air. Plants also mix fresh and polluted air; but rather than forcing one kind of air into another, when oxygen-enriched air is present in, around, and under them, a dilution process results. As polluted air flows around plants and through fresh air, oxygen-rich air is mixed with polluted air and is diluted. Plants also remove from the air other impurities, such as air-borne dirt, sand, fly ash, dust, pollen, smoke, odors, and fumes.

PRECIPITATION AND FILTRATION Mechanical air conditioners filter air through mechanical filters or electrical precipitators to cleanse it. The method of electrical precipitation in air conditioning involves electrically charging air-borne particles, which also carry odors and then collecting these particles on a grid having a strong opposing electrical charge. Plants also collect air-borne particles. The leaves, branches and stems, and pubescence (hairiness) on the leaves and stems trap particles and hold them. The particles are then washed away by the rain and fall to the ground. In addition, plants act as cleaners by absorbing many gaseous and other pollutants directly into their leaves and assimilating them.

Narcosis is a temporary state of depression, and when used in regard to air conditioning, means an area relatively free of turbulence as opposed to its surroundings. This semi-void permits particles to settle out of the contaminant-laden air. A wooded area, or forest, provides such a settling chamber for air pollutants.

AIR WASHING Growing plants transpire a considerable amount of water. A beech tree, for instance, standing alone in the open, loses 75 to 100 gallons of water during a summer

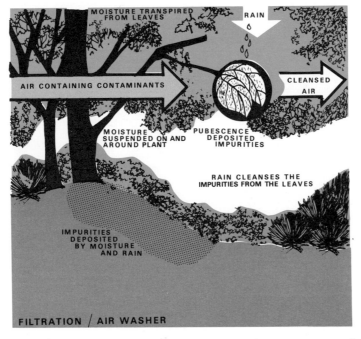

FILTRATION / AIR WASHER

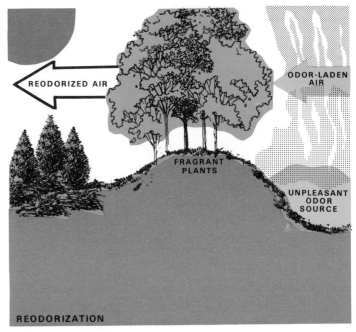

REODORIZATION

day. A mature orchard transpires as much as 600 tons of water per acre per day. Plants transpire large amounts of water into the atmosphere, and cause water to form through the guttation process on their leaves, enabling them to act as air cleaners.

In mechanical air conditioning, air washers are designed to produce contact between air and water for the purpose of obtaining the transfer of heat and moisture between the two and removing impurities from the air. Moisture forming on the leaves as guttation washes particulates off them onto the ground. Moisture in suspension on and around a plant increases the humidity, and settles out wind-borne pollutants.

ODORS Mechanically, fumes and odors are controlled by masking and reoderizing. This is accomplished by replacing obnoxious odors with a stronger, more powerful, bearable or pleasing smell—air conditioners and aerosol atomizers. Fragrant plants may be planted between the source of a disagreeable odor and the recipient to mask the unpleasant odor and provide a pleasant odor in its place. Plants also have the ability to absorb odors directly and metabolize them.

Plants For Pollution Control

Man has invented mechanical means for cleaning and purifying air indoors. Plants can effectively perform these functions out-of-doors. How effective are these natural air cleaners? The following references serve to illustrate the efficiency of plants in removing air-borne contaminants from the atmosphere.

PLANTS AND GASEOUS POLLUTANTS Dr. Aloys Bernatzky, writing on the "Climatic Influences of the Greens and City Planning" says:

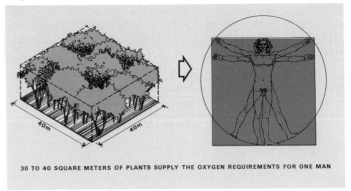

30 TO 40 SQUARE METERS OF PLANTS SUPPLY THE OXYGEN REQUIREMENTS FOR ONE MAN

What green spaces can perform in the interest of the climate of a city is best illustrated by the work done by a single tree. Let us take a free standing beech, 80 to 100 years old. With its crown of 15 meters in width and its height of 25 meters, it covers a spot of 160 square meters. The total surface of all its leaves adds up to 1600 square meters. But this is the outer surface. The inner surface of the leaves, i.e., the total of the cell walls which are active in assimilation, makes up a hundred times as much—according to plant physiologists (Walter)—that is 160,000 square meters.[29]

Expanding on this basic data in a later article entitled, "The Performance and Value of Trees," Bernatzky explains:

The air in which we live and which we daily breathe on an average contains, in . . . (open) country, 0.03 percent by volume of carbon dioxide (CO_2) per cubic meter of air; this means on an average 0.5 g CO_2 or 0.15 g carbon (C) (Strassburger). In cities and industrial areas, this component achieves substantially greater values.

This carbon extracted from carbon dioxide . . . is the principal nutrient of plants. Air flows through the intercellular spaces of the leaves. The carbon dioxide is extracted from the air, and using water and solar energy, processed into glucose and oxygen. This process takes place in accordance with the following equation: 6 molecules CO_2 (carbon dioxide, weighing 264 g) + 6 molecules H_2O (water, 106 g) produce, at a =consumption= of 675 calories, 1 molecule $C_6H_{12}O_6$ (glucose, 180 g) + 6 molecules O (oxygen, 192 g). . . .

Since 1 square meter leaf surface assimilates 1.5 g CO_2 per hour according to Walter, our beech, with its 1600 square meters exterior surface, converts 2400 g carbon dioxide (i.e., the carbon dioxide of 5,000 cu. m. air=the volume of 10 homes) in favorable weather conditions per hour and square meters plus 960 g water, consuming 6075 calories of sunlight, into 1600 g glucose while emitting 1712 g oxygen.

With a height of 25 meters and a crown diameter of 15 meters this one beech, with its roots, trunk, branches and twigs, has a volume of roughly 15 cu. meters dry substance which weighs 800 kg per cu. meter. For the whole tree, this amounts to 12,000 kg. One half of the weight is accounted for by carbon, i.e., 600 kg. As stated above, every cubic meter air contains 0.15 g C or 0.5 g CO_2, the carbon incorporated in the tree stems from the carbon dioxide of 40 million cu. m. air or the volume of 80,000 homes of 500 cu. meters. If the beech is one hundred years old, it has thus annually consumed the carbon dioxide of the air of 800 homes or of 2 homes per day, thus decontaminating the air in respect of carbon dioxide.

Naturally a tree . . . consumes or combusts sugar while consuming oxygen and emitting carbon dioxide, in respiration the reverse process takes place that we have met in assimilation (photosynthesis). On the other hand, the carbon dioxide production of a tree is only $\frac{1}{5}$ to $\frac{1}{3}$ of the quantity of CO_2 which it has consumed· in assimilation (photosynthesis). Accordingly, the consumption of carbon dioxide is vastly larger than the production of carbon dioxide and, respectively, the consumption of oxygen . . .—it is on this that human life rests. . . .

A leaf surface of 25 sq. m. may emit, on a sunny day, as much oxygen as man requires in the same period. But since man breathes also at night and in winter, i.e., at times when there is no assimilation, at least 150 sq. m. of leaf surface are required in order to cover one person's oxygen requirements in a year. Converted to oxygen producing plant surface, an inhabitant of town centers would require 30-40 sq. m. greenery surface (trees, shrubs, plants, grass) in order to cover his requirements.[30]

Dr. A. F. Bush, Professor of Engineering in the Department of Engineering at the University of California, Los Angeles, suggests, in answer to the question of quantification of air pollution functionability of plants, the following approach:

. . . We should develop quantification information; it could be very useful.

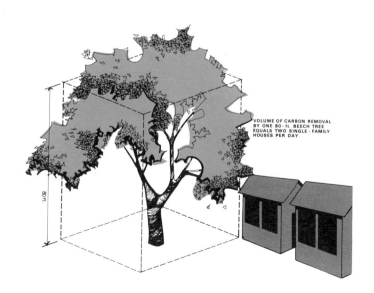

VOLUME OF CARBON REMOVAL BY ONE 80-ft. BEECH TREE EQUALS TWO SINGLE - FAMILY HOUSES PER DAY.

[29]Aloys Bernatzky, "Climatic Influences of Greens and City Planning," *Anthos*, no. 1 (1966), p. 23.

[30]Aloys Bernatzky, "The Performance and Value of Trees," *Anthos*, no. 1 (1969), p. 125.

One approach is to consider a cropped field, such as hay or corn, which can be weighed when harvested and the weight per unit determined. Since most products are cellulosic in nature and have a general formula of $C_6H_{10}O_5$ cellulose, or $C_6H_9O_4$ for trees and bush, the source of the carbon (C_6) is from the CO_2 in the air. It is apparent that it takes some such reaction which might be written:

$$C_6H_{10}O_5 + 6O_2 = 6\,CO_2 + 5\,H_2O$$

$$162\# + 192\# = 264\# + 90\#$$

Going from right to left it can be shown that 264# of CO_2 + 90# of H_2O are required to produce 162# of cellulose material. The release of oxygen would be about 192#. Going from left to right is the combustion process where oxygen is used and carbon dioxide and water vapor are produced.

A high rate of growth may show several tons of cellulose material being produced per acre per month in the growing season when soil, moisture, and climate are favorable.

All of this does little to enlighten us on the amount of pollution removed in the process. One assumption might be made, however, and that is the rate of uptake of other pollutant gases in the air may be the same as CO_2 in ratio to their concentration in the air.[31]

Dr. Paul E. Waggoner, Chief Climatologist at the Connecticut Agricultural Experiment Station, reports on his research as follows:

Our laboratory studies and subsequent computer analysis showed that plants can remove enough ozone from the air to benefit us. For example, we studied what happens when a mass of polluted air containing 150 parts of ozone per billion parts of air (ppb) passes over a forest of trees 15 feet tall.

We chose 150 ppb of ozone as the concentration in the polluted air because this is what we find in the air of Connecticut on a fairly polluted day. The computer analysis told us that if such an air mass stood over the forest for one hour, the air filtering down to the forest floor would have only 60 to 90 ppb of ozone remaining. The rest would have been taken up by the canopy of leaves. If the polluted air mass stood over the forest for eight hours, the air filtering down to the forest floor would have only 30 ppb of ozone left.

These studies told us other things. For instance, taller trees would remove more pollution than would shorter trees. The larger the stomatal pores and the more numerous the stomata per square inch of leaf surface, the more effective are the leaves in removing ozone from the air.

It is satisfying to learn that the plants that we like, because they are making the hills green, are cleansing our air. And it is important to discover and develop the kinds of vegetation that cleans most effectively.[32]

PLANTS AND PARTICULATE POLLUTANTS Plants play an important role in helping to remove particles of pollution from the air. Improvement of the climate of a city is of special importance in the center, where green spaces are already limited and are rapidly disappearing. Green spaces are not interchangeable with buildings, if they are to have an affect on the climate of the city. In other words, a tree cut down in the center of the city cannot be replaced by a tree planted somewhere at the edge to influence the climate. This is brought out by Dr. Bernatzky, writing on the climatic effect of greens in city planning; he says an important feature of parks and large areas of plants in their dust-reducing effect.

. . . To begin with, they produce no dust themselves. Then, if there is no wind, dust elements in the air will settle on the plants in the parks. Measurement taken near the Frankfurt main station and in the town center showed a concentration of 18,000 kernels per air unit, whereas measurements taken at the same time at the Rothschild Park (surface 4 hectares) showed a concentration of not more than 1000 to 3000 kernels per unit.

As concerns dust particles the figures read 3000 in streets planted with trees, compared to 10,000 to 12,000 particles in streets without trees in the same quarter of the town.[33]

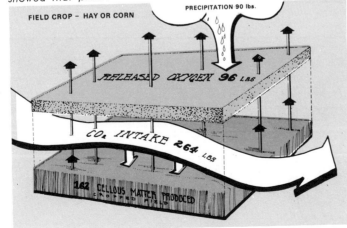

[31]Letter from A. F. Bush to the author, September 24, 1967.
[32]Paul E. Waggoner as quoted by Tom Stevenson in "How Plants Help Fight Against Air Pollution," *Washington Post*, August 2, 1970, sec. H, p. 7.
[33]Bernatzky, "Climatic Influences," p. 24.

The effect of forests and large plantings in removing air-borne and wind-blown particles is discussed by Rudolph Geiger, in his book, **The Climate Near The Ground.**

. . . the passive influence of the forest on the wind field at its edge is much more effective than its active influence. The wind field for its own part is instrumental in controlling two other processes that take place at the forest edge, namely, the dissemination of seeds and distribution of dust. Along a country road at the western edge of a forest on a hot, dusty summer day, the filtering effect of the trees at the border can be seen in the white powder observed over everything. From measure-

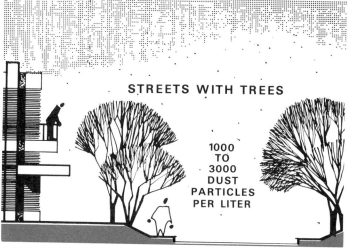

STREETS WITH TREES

1000 TO 3000 DUST PARTICLES PER LITER

10,000 TO 12,000 DUST PARTICLES PER LITER

STREETS WITHOUT TREES

ments made by M. Rotschke, it appears that with winds perpendicular to the forest edge, in addition to the maximum at the edge itself, an increase in dust content is found in the inner border zone. For example, on 29 January 1935, with a wind of 203 m. sec. −1 in the open, the dust content in thousands of particles per liter in front of (−) and behind (+) the forest edge was:

Distance (m)	−100	−50	−25	+25	+50	+100
Dust content	10.1	10.2	10.3	14.0	11.8	11.5

Since in this particular case there was a thin snow cover with a temperature of −2° C, the filtering effect could be observed without interference from any secondary source of dust. The interior of the forest became more and more free of dust. If the wind blows at an angle to the forest edge, there is a marked increase in dust in the outer border zone, which results from the increase in wind mentioned earlier.

The illustration shows the distribution of dust measured by M. Rotschke during an automobile journey near Leipzig in the afternoon of 10 April 1935, using a Zeiss conimeter. Not only the edge, but also the whole area of the forest, which itself produces hardly any dust, shows a low dust content.[34]

Dr. Wilfrid Bach and Edward Mathews prepared a paper entitled "The Importance of Green Areas in Urban Planning" for the workshop, Bioclimatology and Environmental Health, in 1969. In this they made the following statement on "Effects of Green Areas on Air Pollution Levels" by quoting other recognized experts:

Kuehn states bluntly that the belief that green areas are the 'lungs' of the cities is inaccurate. Quoting others he supports this statement with the example that three million acres of green areas would be needed in order to improve the air of Berlin to any marked degree. However, the following examples will show that already very small green areas are able to reduce certain pollutants markedly.

Meldau found that 2.5 acres of beech wood are able to extract about 4 t. of dust per year from the atmosphere and bind it into the humus layer. Pindard and Wilkins and also Meetham report of a 28% reduction in smoke concentration in Hyde Park which is only of 1 sq. mile in area. Accompanying figure shows the decrease in smoke concentration in Hyde Park as a function of wind direction. Wainwright and Wilson measured SO_2 in Hyde Park with portable apparatus and found that the rate of decrease of SO_2 with the distance from the upwind

[34]Rudolph Geiger, *The Climate Near the Ground* (Cambridge, 1950), p. 346.

edge was closely related to the lapse rate but not to the wind speed.

In an older publication, Landsberg states that a 600 ft. wide belt of planting can reduce dust count by as much as 75 percent. Even lawns act as dust filters.

A Russian study conducted by Kalyuzhnyi et al. shows an enormous effect of so-called sanitary clearance zones which are green areas surrounding factories. They found that a 500 m. wide green area reduces SO_2 concentration by 70 percent and nitric oxide concentration by 67 percent.

In a more recent study in the United States, Neuberger et al. found that a dense coniferous forest reduced the concentration of ragweed-pollen by 80%. Deciduous trees were less effective. Also the sub-microscopic Aitken nuclei (0.1 um) were reduced by coniferous trees on the average of 34% and through deciduous trees by 19%. Even radioactive aerosols are filtered out by green areas. Herbst (cit. Keuhn 8) measured 2-4 times higher radioactivity on the windward than on the leeward side of trees.

The effect of a city park, which had already been brought about by the temperature and the humidity variations, is now further emphasized by the variations of average SO_2 and particularly by average smoke concentration in Sheffield. The clean air effect of Norfolk Park reaches right into and beyond the city center and is a real phenomenon, since it could be found in 8 years of investigations." [35]

From the preceding, it can be seen that plants can and do function as air cleansing agents to oxygenate and remove gaseous particles and odors from the atmosphere. Plants of adequate sizes and types are effective as air cleansers.

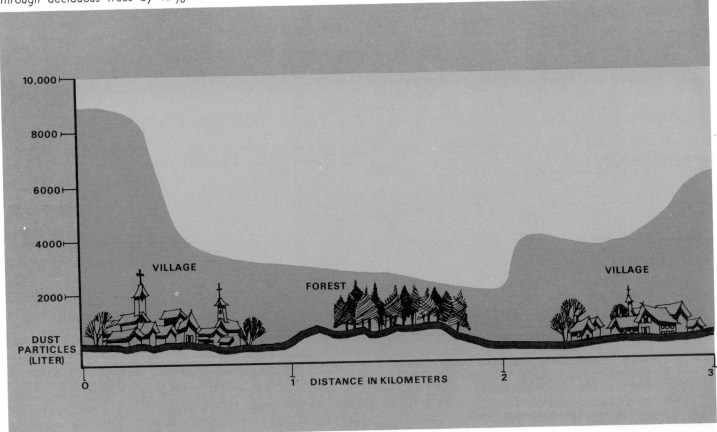

[35]Bach and Mathews, p. 16.

TRAFFIC CONTROL

The purpose of this section is to discuss the functions of plants as traffic controlling elements. As one moves through an area, if the direction of movement is planned and controlled, the experience may be more enjoyable than if the direction of movement is random and uncontrolled. When random movement through an area is permitted, the area may be damaged and destroyed and the environmental quality reduced. The environmental designer, when planning walks, drives, and other traffic ways, must consider the predictable movement of pedestrians, animals, and vehicles. When these needs have been considered, then the traffic circulation systems may be designed.

Plants For Traffic Control

Plants may be used to assist in controlling traffic, while adding to the visual quality of the environment. Plants can be used to control bicycles, automobiles, motorcycles, pedestrians, and animals.

PLANT RATING SYSTEM FOR PEDESTRIAN CONTROL

Plants enhance the beauty of an area when they are used to direct people through it in a definite pattern or direction. More often than not, fences, chains, posts, and wires, when used to control and direct traffic, destroy the natural beauty of an area.

By the use of plants, the beauty of an area may be enhanced rather than destroyed. The designer must ask himself: Which plants are good for traffic control? The rating system which follows will give the designer criteria by which to answer this question. Before considering plants to control traffic, the designer must decide how much control is needed. It may be that no plants are necessary or that a lawn panel will handle the situation. It may be that ground cover, a low hedge, a high hedge, large plants, or even a combination of plants is necessary.

When the type of barrier for traffic control has been determined, the following factors should be considered in evaluating and selecting the plants to be used:

- ☐ Characteristic of the plant variety.
- ☐ Ultimate height of the plant.
- ☐ Spacing or planting density of the plants.
- ☐ Eventual desired width of the plantings.

An efficiency rating system for plants could be based on 10 possible degrees of effectiveness for each of the four factors: a "10" rating for maximum effectiveness and a "1" rating for minimum effectiveness.

The unique characteristics of some plants make them more suitable for controlling traffic than others. Characteristics are rated according to number of stems, whether thorn or thornless, with stiff or flexible branches, and density.

Sixteen possible combinations of these variables, are:

SINGLE STEM, NO THORNS, FLEXIBLE

SINGLE STEM, NO THORNS, STIFF

SINGLE STEM, THORNS, FLEXIBLE

SINGLE STEM, THORNS, STIFF

MULTI-STEM, NO THORNS, OPEN-FLEXIBLE

MULTI-STEM, NO THORNS, LESS OPEN-FLEXIBLE

MULTI-STEM, NO THORNS, DENSE-FLEXIBLE

MULTI-STEM, NO THORNS, OPEN-STIFF

MULTI-STEM, NO THORNS, LESS OPEN-STIFF

MULTI-STEM, NO THORNS, DENSE-STIFF

MULTI-STEM, THORNS, OPEN-FLEXIBLE

MULTI-STEM, THORNS, LESS OPEN-FLEXIBLE

MULTI-STEM, THORNS, DENSE-FLEXIBLE

MULTI-STEM, THORNS, OPEN-STIFF

MULTI-STEM, THORNS, LESS-OPEN-STIFF

MULTI-STEM, THORNS, DENSE-STIFF

Since some of these are nearly equal in their effectiveness in controlling traffic, they could be placed on a 10-point characteristic scale. These 10 divisions are:

1. Single-stem—no thorns—flexible branches.
2. Single-stem—no thorns—stiff branches.
3. Multi-stem—no thorns—flexible branches—open.
4. Multi-stem—no thorns—flexible branches—less open.
   Multi-stem—no thorns—stiff branches—open.
5. Multi-stem—no thorns—stiff branches—dense.
   Single stem—thorns—flexible branches.
6. Single-stem—thorns—stiff branches.
7. Multi-stem—thorns—flexible branches—open.
8. Multi-stem—thorns—flexible—less open.
   Multi-stem—thorns—stiff branches—open.
9. Multi-stem—thorns—flexible—dense.
   Multi-stem—thorns—stiff—less open.
10. Multi-stem—thorns—stiff branches—dense.

The plants' ultimate height, when mature, is the next factor to be rated. In rating plants on height, the system extends from 3 inches or less, to 5 feet or more.

The 10 dimensions are:

1. 0 to 3"
2. 3" to 6"
3. 6" to 12"
4. 12" to 18"
5. 18" to 24"
6. 24" to 30"
7. 30" to 3'
8. 3' to 4'
9. 4' to 5'
10. 5' and higher.

HEIGHT

PSYCHOLOGICAL   PHYSICAL

Spacing is important to consider, since plants, regardless of their characteristics or height, are ineffective in controlling traffic if they are sparsely spaced, allowing movement through the openings between them. In rating plants for spacing, the system extends from greater than 30 inches to less than 6 inches.

The ratings are:

1. 30" and wider
2. 27" to 30"
3. 24" to 27"
4. 21" to 24"
5. 18" to 21"
6. 15" to 18"
7. 12" to 15"
8. 9" to 12"
9. 6" to 9"
10. 6" and narrower.

SPACING OR DENSITY

Plant width is a major factor in determining effectiveness of plants for controlling traffic. As an example, grass or a ground cover may be an effective barrier if the lawn or planting-bed is wide enough; yet in a narrow area, even a medium hedge may not be adequate.

In rating planting widths the system extends "1" to "10," as follows:

1. 6"
2. 9"
3. 12"
4. 18"
5. 2'
6. 3'
7. 4'
8. 6'
9. 8'
10. wider than 8'.

Some plants have a spread or width of more than 8 feet, making them effective barriers when planted in a single row. Others with less width may be planted in multiple rows.

WIDTH

Since the relative effectiveness of plants in controlling pedestrian traffic can be categorized, an existing or potential planting may be rated on the basis of a possible 10 points of each of the four factors. Four is the lowest possible rating and 40 designates a perfect traffic control plant. The total rating system is:

T-C number (Traffic Control)	Degree of effectiveness
4–10	minimum
10–20	average
20–30	good
30–40	excellent

EXAMPLES OF RATED PLANTS To further illustrate how the system works, some representative plants could be rated.

Rosa rugosa—Rugosa rose is a sturdy shrub with stout upright stems, forming a dense mass. Ultimate height is from 4 to 6 feet with a similar spread. The characteristic rating factor for this shrub is 6, under single stem thorns with stiff branches. The height rating factor is 9. Spread at 15 inches, the density rating factor is 7, and the width rating factor is also 7. Under the numerical grading, Rugosa rose has a total of 29 points, making it a good pedestrian traffic control plant.

Rosa hugonis—Father Hugo's rose ranges from 6 to 10 feet in height, with a 10-to-12-foot spread. Its form is a rounded mass with arching branches carrying the foliage to the ground. Characteristic rating 5, height rating 10, density (at 18 inches) rating 6, width rating 10, total rating 31 (excellent).

Ribes alpinum—Alpine or mountain currant is a dense and twiggy rounded shrub with foliage to the ground. It has a 3-to-6-foot height with a 3-to-10-foot spread. Characteristic rating 5, height 5, density (at 15 inches) 7, width 9, total 26 (good).

Rhamnus cathartica—Buckthorn is a large rounded shrub fairly dense with branches and foliage to the ground, has 12-foot height, with a 10-to-12-foot spread. Characteristic rating 9, height 10, density (at 18 inches) 6, width 10, total 35 (excellent).

Physocarpus opulifolius—Ninebark is a loose, wide-spreading shrub with recurving branches rounded and fairly dense with foliage, with a height and spread of 10 feet. Characteristic rating 4, height rating 10, density (at 18 inches) 6, width 10, total rating 30 (excellent).

With this system the environmental designers can rate all plants for traffic control use.

PLANTS FOR VEHICULAR TRAFFIC CONTROL Some limited research has been done on the ability of plants to function as effective vehicle barriers. One of the most significant studies in automobile traffic control on highways was conducted by Andrew J. White of Motor Vehicle Research, Inc. (1953).[36] He performed a series of crash tests to evaluate the suitability of *Rosa multiflora* and to determine its characteristics which make it suitable for vehicular traffic control. In these tests a fully loaded, 1953 Willys coupe weighing 3,128 pounds was used. At 20 miles per hour (mph) the car penetrated 9.8 feet into the planting. The occupants reported no discomfort experiencing 1.3Gs of deceleration (similar to a fast stop). The car suffered no damage and backed out under its own power. At 30 mph, penetration was 11 feet with only minor dents and chrome scratches; the occupants used no seat belts. In another test, the car traveling 47 mph penetrated 20 feet into the planting with only minor dents and scratches. In the last two tests the car had to be towed out of the planting, but was able to proceed on its own power from that point.

In tests, resilient canes of *Rosa multiflora* withstood 60 pounds per inch pull, while the pull exerted on the canes generated by the penetration by a car was 39 to 43 pounds per inch. The plants used along highways should be resilient rather than rigid to prevent damage to the automobile or injury to passengers when a crash occurs.

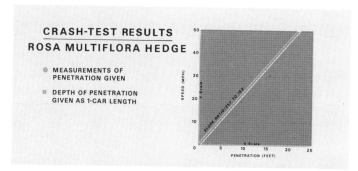

CRASH-TEST RESULTS
ROSA MULTIFLORA HEDGE

● MEASUREMENTS OF PENETRATION GIVEN

■ DEPTH OF PENETRATION GIVEN AS 1-CAR LENGTH

SPEED (MPH)
Y Scale
SLOPE RATIO 53.7 TO 18X
X Scale
PENETRATION (FEET)

[36]Andrew J. White, *Study of Marginal and Median Tree and Shrub Plantings as Safety Barriers on Highways* (South Lee, N. H., 1953) pp. 3-8.

GLARE AND REFLECTION CONTROL

Modern man lives in a "shiny" world. His smooth, polished, and highly reflective building materials accentuate and bounce off the natural daylight from buildings, streets, automobiles, and other objects causing visual discomfort. At night, street lights, safety lights, advertising signs, and automobile headlights produce glare and are reflected. Early morning and late afternoon sun can be a nuisance also as it reflects off the water's surface and into windows. The assault continues with more glass being used to open up interiors, blending them with the landscape.

Many architectural elements have been used to solve these problems. Canvas, aluminum, and fiberglass awnings blunt and block the sun's rays. Fences, walls, and screens are used for this purpose. The orientation of a building must be considered to avoid excessive glare and reflection.

Plants screen, blunt, or soften glare and reflection. The degree to which they can do this depends upon their height, density, and location. This has often been overlooked. Many architectural elements used to solve these problems have the disadvantage of hardness, excessive cost, inflexibility, and lack naturalness. Glare and reflection problems can often be solved while adding to beauty by using plants. Before discussing further how plants can or should be used, a definition of glare and reflection is necessary.

Primary Glare

Glare has three factors—a bright light source; atmospheric hindrances such as dust, haze, and humidity; and a viewer whose eyes are offended by the brightness of the source. The bright light source when viewed directly may be called primary glare. Light rays traveling in straight lines are interrupted by atmospheric hindrances causing them to scatter so that it appears to the viewer that he is surrounded by light. Primary light source still creates glare. The daylight source of primary glare is the sun, regardless of its angle in the sky. Night sources include building, street, and floodlights, and advertising signs. Mobile sources include vehicle lights, beacons, and searchlights.

Reflection

Reflection has four factors—a light source, atmospheric hind-rances, a viewer, and an effective reflector. Reflection or reflected glare may be called *secondary glare*. Other elements that govern reflection are the smoothness of reflectivity of the surface, angle of incidence, and amount of light from the source. Air temperature and seasonal conditions, including atmospheric conditions, also affect reflection.

The strength or brightness of reflection or secondary glare depend as much upon the reflective surface as upon the light source.

NATURAL REFLECTIVE SURFACES Some natural surfaces which reflect are water, sand, fields of grains, and rock formations.

MANMADE REFLECTORS Examples of manmade reflectors include glass, metal, chromium plated and enameled automobile parts, glass, metal, brick, stone, painted architectural materials, and concrete, flagstone, colored asphalt, or other paving surfaces.

Working with these basic principles in mind, the designer can use plants to reduce glare or reflection.

Plants Reduce Glare and Reflection

When the sources of glare and reflection are identified and a determination made of the amount of reduction wanted, then the proper plants, having the correct ultimate size, shape, and foliage density can be selected and placed.

Control of glare from reflection ranges from almost complete stoppage of light, to a minor filtering and diffusion, by placing plants between the light source and the viewer. When dealing with reflection, there are two possible points of interception—before light strikes a reflective surface or after it strikes the reflector, yet before it reaches the viewer's eyes.

PRIMARY GLARE REDUCTION Plants may be used to block or filter unwanted primary glare, either during the day or night. Care should be taken to select plants of the proper height and density and to place them so that they will continue to give glare protection during immaturity and maturity.

Plants near windows assist in sun control. Anyone who has ever been awakened by the sun understands the need for sun con-

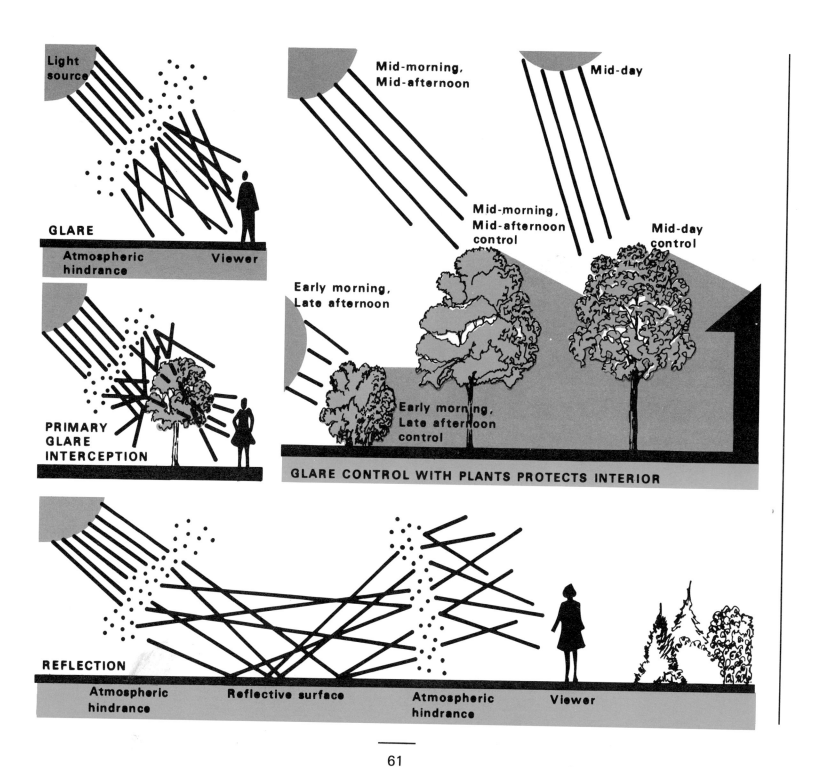

Light source

GLARE

Atmospheric hindrance

Viewer

PRIMARY GLARE INTERCEPTION

Mid-morning, Mid-afternoon

Mid-day

Mid-morning, Mid-afternoon control

Mid-day control

Early morning, Late afternoon

Early morning, Late afternoon control

GLARE CONTROL WITH PLANTS PROTECTS INTERIOR

REFLECTION

Atmospheric hindrance

Reflective surface

Atmospheric hindrance

Viewer

trol. Drapes, blinds, and curtains are used at windows but the smallest opening permits disturbing glare.

Another example of the use for primary daylight glare control is in highway plantings. These should be designed to filter early morning and late afternoon sun to prevent it from blinding the eyes of drivers.

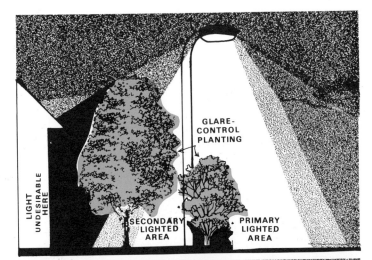

GLARE CONTROL FOR HIGHWAYS

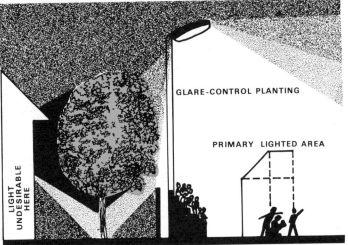

In considering plants for primary daylight glare, it must be remembered that for some locations the winter sun may be welcomed, but the summer sun may be too brilliant for comfort. In that case deciduous plants could be used.

Stationary, primary night light, as well as a high or moving light source is blocked most effectively when the plants are placed close to the viewer. Night lights—moving and stationary, infringing into parts of the environment, such as terraces, patios, and windows, and into the eyes of drivers—can be effectively blocked by judicious selection and placement of plants.

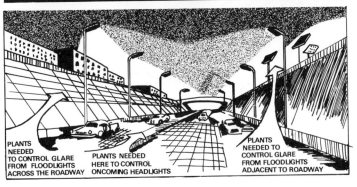

CONTROL OF MOBILE AND STATIONARY NIGHT LIGHTS

PLANTS NEEDED TO CONTROL MOVING NIGHT LIGHTS

REFLECTION REDUCTION Secondary glare, or reflection, as described earlier, results from an excessively bright light, natural or manmade, bounced off a reflective surface. Plants may be used to reduce the intensity of secondary glare by placement to intercept the light before it strikes the reflective surface, or after it strikes a reflector, yet before it reaches the viewer's eyes.

It may be difficult to intercept the light before it strikes a reflective surface, as in the case of a large body of water; but it may be possible to block or filter the light, after it is bounced from the reflector, before it reaches the viewer. The angle at which light strikes the reflective surface depends on the seasons or time of day, and determines where plants should be placed.

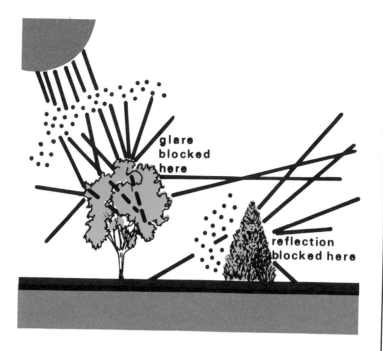

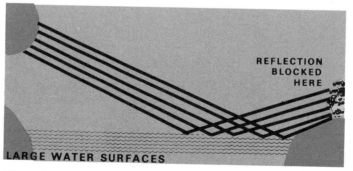

LARGE WATER SURFACES

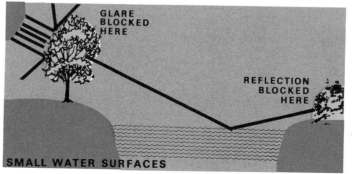

SMALL WATER SURFACES

When it is difficult or impossible to place plants to block glare from a body of water without destroying the view, they may be placed to take advantage of prevailing winds, and thus create a rippling effect on the surface, reducing the reflection.

Sand or paving, both highly reflective, are quite often near water, causing the area to be bright with reflected secondary glare. To de-emphasize the glare and ease the viewer's eyes, a dark, shaded retreat may be provided by plantings of dark foliage and heavy texture. This enables the area to be used for sunbathing without the discomforts of unrelieved glare or brightness. Secondary glare or reflection from paving and pools is prevalent where the surroundings are manmade, but may be ameliorated with plants. Large expanses of paving are highly reflective. Plants may be placed to soften or break up the sun's rays over these areas.

Secondary glare, reflected from the metal and glass on automobiles or the paving of parking lots, can be relieved with judicious selection and careful placement of plants. Sun reflected from contemporary buildings of glass and metal should be filtered or blocked by plants. The essential principle of secondary glare control is to relate the plant to the light source, either between the source and the reflector, or the reflector and the viewer.

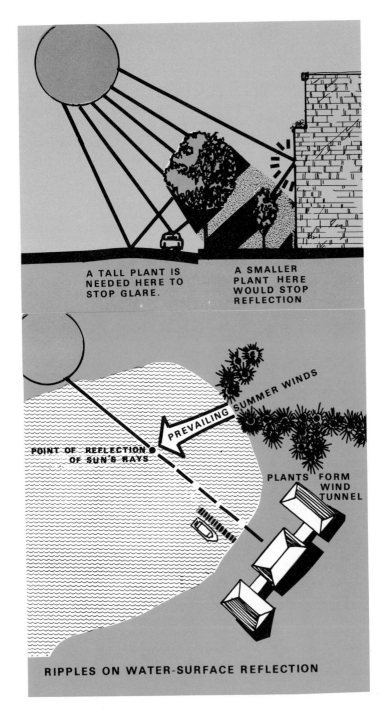

A TALL PLANT IS NEEDED HERE TO STOP GLARE.

A SMALLER PLANT HERE WOULD STOP REFLECTION

RIPPLES ON WATER-SURFACE REFLECTION

PREVAILING SUMMER WINDS

POINT OF REFLECTION OF SUN'S RAYS

PLANTS FORM WIND TUNNEL

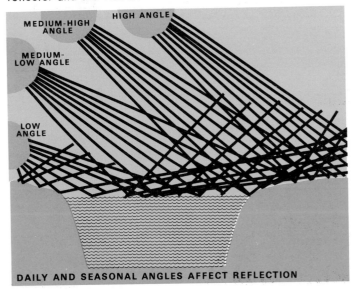

HIGH ANGLE

MEDIUM-HIGH ANGLE

MEDIUM-LOW ANGLE

LOW ANGLE

DAILY AND SEASONAL ANGLES AFFECT REFLECTION

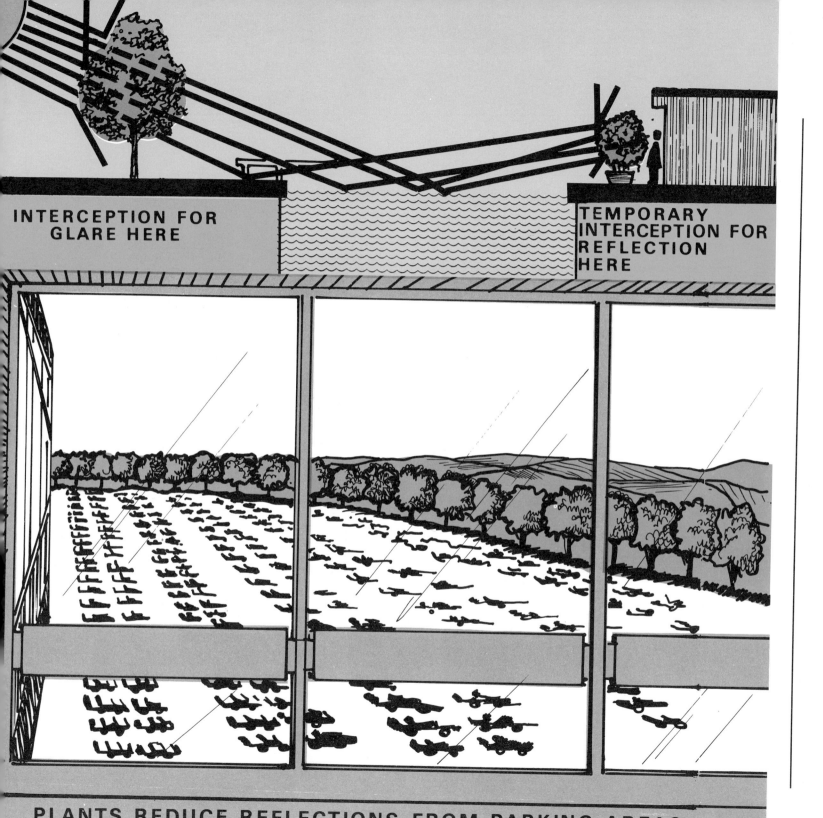

INTERCEPTION FOR GLARE HERE

TEMPORARY INTERCEPTION FOR REFLECTION HERE

PLANTS REDUCE REFLECTIONS FROM PARKING AREAS

climatological uses
of plants

An elementary knowledge of several sciences and disciplines is required for using plants for climate control. The purpose of this chapter is to introduce the reader to some sources of this information and to provide him with a guide for further study. Most available information is from research on plants in a natural state.

The designer should evaluate human requirements for comfort, evaluate existing climatic conditions, and select proper plants for the type and degree of climate control desired.

Man's physical strength and mental activity function best within a given range of climatic conditions. Outside of this range his efficiency lessens; stress and the possibility of disease increase. Within this range he is comfortable and can function efficiently.

The four major elements of climate which affect human comfort are air temperature, solar radiation, air movement, and humidity or precipitation. A microclimate in which these do not place undue stress upon the human body falls within the human "comfort zone." The comfort zone varies with people both within an area and in different areas of the world, either because of inherited or cultural characteristics. Most women prefer a temperature a few degrees warmer than men; young people prefer a temperature a few degrees cooler than the elderly, and Eskimos prefer cooler temperature than Africans. However, there is a general comfort zone which is suitable for most people most of the time.

A human receives and also gives off heat. He receives by absorption, directly from the sun or from reflective objects, and also from other radiation, or by conduction. He acts as a radiator, giving off heat, and heat is conducted away from him. When a balance of heat gain and loss is present, man is comfortable; but if too great an imbalance occurs, he is uncomfortable.

Some writers consider sunstroke or heatstroke as the upper temperature limit for man's existence; with the freezing point as the lower limit. The ideal air temperature may be assumed to be midway between these extremes. Experiments on animals in a variable temperature tunnel at the John B. Pierce Foundation showed that animals preferred to stay at 70°F. about midway between the points calling for maximum expenditure of energy in adjustment to the environment. Therefore, some writers believe that the human being, with a body temperature averaging 98.6° F., seeks a comfortable temperature condition, an area where the temperature is about halfway between what he can tolerate in cold without being grossly uncomfortable and the point which would require real effort on the part of his circulatory and sweat secretion system in order to permit him to adapt to heat.[1]

Dr. H. M. Vernon and T. Bedford, of the British Department of Scientific and Industrial Research, believe that the comfort zone is from 66.1° to 72.1° F. in winter. S. F. Markham believes the range of temperature from 60° to 76° F. is ideal for man.[2] C. E. P. Brooks has indicated that the temperature comfort zone for British people lies between 58° and 70° F.[3] Others have said that the temperature comfort zone in the United States lies between 69° and 80° F.

Interior microclimates are controlled. A comfortable microclimate for humans can be created interiorly by use of heat, air

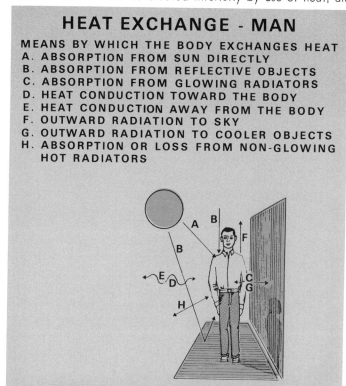

HEAT EXCHANGE - MAN

MEANS BY WHICH THE BODY EXCHANGES HEAT
A. ABSORPTION FROM SUN DIRECTLY
B. ABSORPTION FROM REFLECTIVE OBJECTS
C. ABSORPTION FROM GLOWING RADIATORS
D. HEAT CONDUCTION TOWARD THE BODY
E. HEAT CONDUCTION AWAY FROM THE BODY
F. OUTWARD RADIATION TO SKY
G. OUTWARD RADIATION TO COOLER OBJECTS
H. ABSORPTION OR LOSS FROM NON-GLOWING HOT RADIATORS

[1]H. M. Vernon and T. Bedford, "Environmental Warmth and Human Comfort," *British Journal of Applied Physics* (February 1950), pp. 33-38.

[2]S. F. Markham, *Climate and the Energy of Nations* (London, 1947), p. 143.

[3]C. E. P. Brooks, *Climate in Everyday Life* (London, 1950), p. 53.

conditioning, and illumination. Such positive control is not possible exteriorly, but some degree of control is needed for human comfort and use. Wind, solar radiation, precipitation of all types, and excessive temperature variations are factors to be considered.

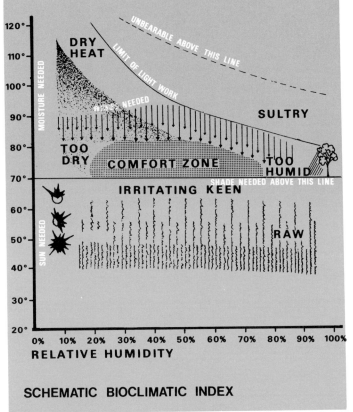

SCHEMATIC BIOCLIMATIC INDEX

A bioclimatic evaluation is necessary before designing for a climatic balance. Prevailing climatic conditions can be plotted on a chart to show what corrective measures are needed. A bioclimatic chart is an excellent way to portray temperature and humidity. A chart is shown which applies to the inhabitants of the moderate climatic zones in the United States, at elevations not in excess of 1,000 feet above sea level, with customary indoor clothing in a sedentary condition, or doing light work.

When the bioclimatic conditions—air temperature, solar radia-

tion, wind, and humidity—have been evaluated, a determination of the type and degree of climate control necessary to provide human comfort can be made. A sun shade, a wind screen, a canopy to deflect rain or to cool, or combinations of all of these can be used to control or ameliorate climate. In addition, walls, fences, earth forms, and free-standing roofed structures may be used. Objects or elements may alter the climate positively or negatively. They may ameliorate or aggravate climatic problems—that is, they may either increase or decrease man's comfort.

Plants play a significant role in climate control, but their capabilities have not been as well researched as other climatic control elements. However, of all the functional abilities of plants, this function has been the most completely indexed. This has been done mostly with plants in a natural, rural state, primarily for agricultural purposes, and the information has only peripheral relevance for climate control in congested urban or suburban situations. More study is required to determine the effectiveness of plants in these situations.

What plants can do to control climate, how they do it, and how effective they are will be discussed in the following sections on solar radiation control, wind control, precipitation control, and temperature control.

SOLAR RADIATION CONTROL

The sun is the source of the earth's climate. Radiant heat in solar radiation may be either desirable or undesirable, depending upon geographic location, season, and air temperature surrounding the recipient.

As light and heat in the form of solar radiation come from the sun, a variety of things occur. Part of it is reflected into space from clouds over the earth; part is scattered and diffused into the sky vault as it strikes small particles in the earth's atmosphere; and part of it is absorbed by carbon dioxide, water vapor, and ozone in the atmosphere. The remainder, approximately one-fifth, penetrates directly through the atmosphere to the earth's surface where it is either absorbed or reflected.

As a result, solar radiation may be received as direct radiation from the sun, as reflected radiation from atmospheric particles

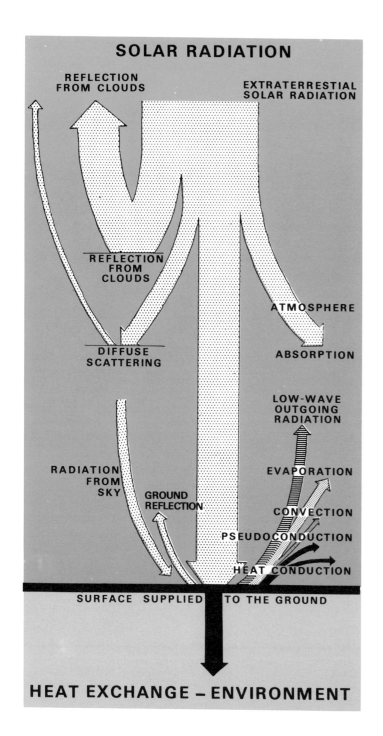

SOLAR RADIATION

REFLECTION FROM CLOUDS

EXTRATERRESTIAL SOLAR RADIATION

REFLECTION FROM CLOUDS

ATMOSPHERE

DIFFUSE SCATTERING

ABSORPTION

LOW-WAVE OUTGOING RADIATION

RADIATION FROM SKY

GROUND REFLECTION

EVAPORATION

CONVECTION

PSEUDOCONDUCTION

HEAT CONDUCTION

SURFACE SUPPLIED   TO THE GROUND

HEAT EXCHANGE – ENVIRONMENT

found in the sky vault, or as reflected radiation from materials on or near the earth surface.

Radiation is undoubtedly the most important of all meteorologic elements. It is the source of power that drives the atmospheric circulation, the only means of exchange of energy between the earth and the rest of the universe, and the basis for organizing our daily lives.
—Rudolph Geiger [4]

Radiant heat transfer has been categorized as five types. These are: direct shortwave radiation from the sun; diffused shortwave radiation from the sky vault; shortwave radiation reflected from the surrounding terrain; longwave radiation from the heated ground and nearby objects; and outgoing longwave radiation exchange from building to sky. This discussion is concerned with the first four types of heat transfer as they relate to solar radiation.

The approximate one-fifth of the solar radiation that pene-

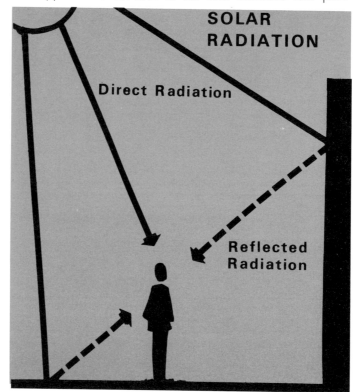

SOLAR RADIATION

Direct Radiation

Reflected Radiation

[4]Rudolph Geiger, *The Climate Near the Ground* (Cambridge, 1950), p. 346.

trates the atmosphere and reaches the earth's surface is direct solar radiation.

Diffused shortwave radiation occurs when, upon striking the atmosphere, solar radiation is reflected off minute particles of dust and other substances in the atmosphere bouncing back and forth among the particles until it finally reaches the earth's surface. Since it appears to come from the entire sky, it is referred to as radiation from the sky vault. Part of the shortwave solar radiation is absorbed by the atmosphere and by the particles in the atmosphere causing them to become warm. The warmth a recipient feels from the atmosphere is referred to as incident radiation.

Part of the solar radiation that strikes the earth's surface is absorbed by the ground, buildings, plants, and animals, thus heating the objects absorbing it. The heated objects in turn re-radiate heat and it is this re-radiated heat that is referred to as long-wave heat radiation.

Reflected shortwave radiation is solar radiation which strikes the earth and is not absorbed but is reflected. Surfaces have varying degrees of reflectivity; and the degree of reflection of solar radiation for a given surface is referred to as the albedo rate. It is expressed as the percentage of reflectivity of both

the direct solar radiation and the diffused radiation from the sky vault. Albedo rates for various surfaces are illustrated in the accompanying charts.

Since solar radiation, may be direct, or may be radiated either directly or incidentally, or may be reflected, control of solar radiation is based upon interception, either by obstruction-filtration or by reflection reduction.

Various solar radiation control devices are used between man and the sun, or between reflective or radiating surfaces and man. Some of these are architectural elements such as canvas awnings, darkened surfaces, and various other wood, steel, stone, plastic, and cloth interpositional devices.

Plants Control Solar Radiation

Trees, shrubs, ground covers, and turf are among the best exterior solar radiation control devices. This has been and is one of the major functional uses of plants, both in tropical climates where solar radiation is oppressive, requiring year-round control, and in temperate climates where solar radiation is most oppressive in summer, requiring seasonal control.

A single plant or a grouping of plants may be used to control direct solar radiation by shading the sun, or by intercepting

ALBEDO OF VARIOUS SURFACES FOR TOTAL SOLAR RADIATION WITH DIFFUSE REFLECTION	%
Fresh snow cover	75—95
Dense cloud cover	60—90
Old snow cover	40—70
Clean, firm snow	50—65
Light sand dunes, surf	30—60
Clean glacier ice	30—46
Dirty, firm snow	20—50
Dirty, glacier ice	20—30
Sandy soil	15—40
Meadows and fields	12—30
Densely built-up areas	15—25
Woods	5—20
Dark cultivated soil	7—10
Water surfaces, sea	3—10

PERCENT OF INCIDENT SOLAR RADIATION DIFFUSELY REFLECTED	
NATURE OF SURFACE	ESTIMATE % REFLECTED
Bare ground, dry	10—25
Bare ground, wet	8—9
Sand, dry	18—30
Sand, wet	9—18
Mold, black, dry	14
Mold, black, wet	8
Rock	12—15
Dry grass	32
Green fields	3—15
Green leaves	25—32
Dark forest	5
Desert	21—28
Salt flats	12
Bark (depending on color)	23—48
Asphalt	15
City area	10

PLANTS CONTROL
SOLAR RADIATION

reflected radiation from some surface. Solar radiation can be intercepted, either before it strikes or after it is reflected, in much the same manner as glare is intercepted.

INTERCEPTION   Plants used for interception of solar radiation may completely block the sun's rays or filter them. Obstruction occurs when plants with dense foliage, multiple layers, or a dense canopy are used. Filtration occurs when plants with open, loose foliage are used.

Part of the sun's radiation is absorbed, reflected, and transmitted through the leaves. The sun's rays are filtered through the

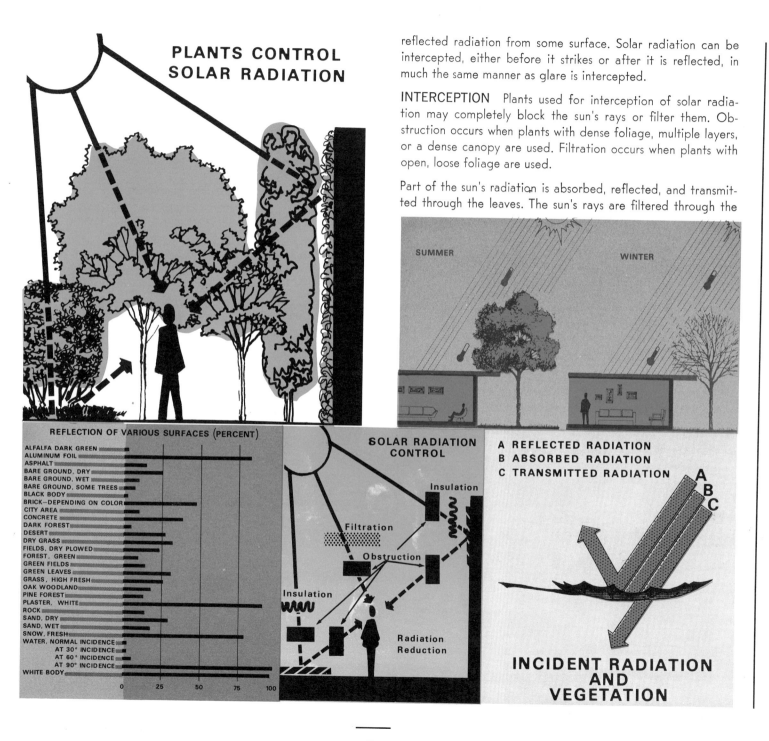

SUMMER   WINTER

REFLECTION OF VARIOUS SURFACES (PERCENT)

ALFALFA DARK GREEN
ALUMINUM FOIL
ASPHALT
BARE GROUND, DRY
BARE GROUND, WET
BARE GROUND, SOME TREES
BLACK BODY
BRICK—DEPENDING ON COLOR
CITY AREA
CONCRETE
DARK FOREST
DESERT
DRY GRASS
FIELDS, DRY PLOWED
FOREST, GREEN
GREEN FIELDS
GREEN LEAVES
GRASS, HIGH FRESH
OAK WOODLAND
PINE FOREST
PLASTER, WHITE
ROCK
SAND, DRY
SAND, WET
SNOW, FRESH
WATER, NORMAL INCIDENCE
          AT 30° INCIDENCE
          AT 60° INCIDENCE
          AT 90° INCIDENCE
WHITE BODY

0   25   50   75   100

SOLAR RADIATION
CONTROL

Insulation

Filtration

Obstruction

Insulation

Radiation
Reduction

A REFLECTED RADIATION
B ABSORBED RADIATION
C TRANSMITTED RADIATION

A
B
C

INCIDENT RADIATION
AND
VEGETATION

leaves of deciduous trees with relatively light foliage. A measurable amount of cooling occurs beneath plants that intercept solar radiation. It is cooler beneath a plant that completely obstructs than one that filters solar radiation.

Deciduous plants in full leaf are the best solar radiation control devices when the sun's rays are most oppressive in temperate climates. When the leaves have been shed, the rays of the sun and its resultant heat are usually pleasing. A coniferous tree casts a year-round shadow pattern of approximately the same extent and degree, and may be more desirable in tropical climates.

Each plant variety casts its own distinctive shadow both in shape and density. For example, maples, oaks, and beeches cast dark, dense shadows, and trees such as honey-locust and willow-oak cast fine, light, lacy shadows. A vine on a trellis or other architectural structure gives seasonal shade as needed.

Studies have been made on the relative efficiency of red beech with dense foliage in the interception of sunlight, and on the relative light intensity inside and outside stands of deciduous and evergreen trees.

Measurement was recorded of light intensity in deciduous stands, both with and without foliage. The accompanying illustrations give the percentage of light reaching the ground through plants and show the relative efficiency of plants in the interception of solar radiation.

Another study indicates that in a dense tropical rain forest,

with trees of approximately 30 meters in height, only 1 percent of the outside light reaches an area 2 meters above the forest floor and at times only .04 to .05 percent of the outside light reaches the forest floor.

REFLECTION REDUCTION   A light, smooth surface reflects more of the sun's rays than a coarse, dark surface. Plants generally have a rougher, darker surface than any manmade paving or architectural materials and, as a consequence, reflect less solar radiation than a smooth surface. This is because the multi-faceted surfaces presented by the leaves of plants reflect and diffuse direct solar radiation. To be effective, plants may be introduced either before or after the rays of the sun strike a reflective surface. A dark plant, with a smaller leaf surface, is more effective in breaking down reflection. Conifers, other needled, or small-leafed plants with pubescent surfaces greatly decrease solar radiation reflectivity. To lessen the intensity of the heat and light reflected from paving or sidewalks, vines growing up on a building wall or as ground cover provide a buffer against solar radiation.

Trees, shrubs, ground cover, and turf, or even a combination of these, are effective in reducing direct as well as reflected solar radiation. They absorb the heat, provide shade for walls and ground surfaces, and create dead air spaces. Thus plants provide insulation for buildings and the earth, not only from the intense heat of solar radiation, but also from abrupt temperature changes. Plants absorb more of the sun's heat during the day and release it slowly in the evening—not only cooling

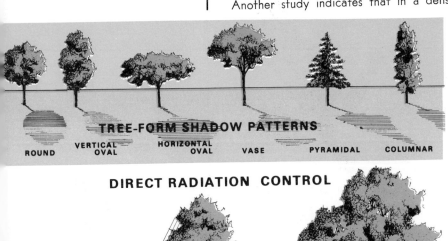

TREE-FORM SHADOW PATTERNS

ROUND   VERTICAL OVAL   HORIZONTAL OVAL   VASE   PYRAMIDAL   COLUMNAR

DIRECT RADIATION CONTROL

PERFORATED CANOPY   SINGLE-LAYER CANOPY   MULTIPLE-LAYER CANOPY

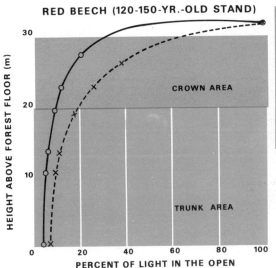

RED BEECH (120-150-YR.-OLD STAND)

HEIGHT ABOVE FOREST FLOOR (m)

CROWN AREA

TRUNK AREA

PERCENT OF LIGHT IN THE OPEN

CLOUDY ------   SUNNY ——

LIGHT INTENSITY (% OF THAT OUTSIDE) IN STANDS OF TREES		
TYPE OF TREE (OLD STAND)	NO FOLIAGE	FOLIAGE
Deciduous		
Red beech	26—66	2—40
Oak	43—69	3—35
Ash	39—80	8—60
Birch		20—30
Evergreen		
Silver fir		2—20
Spruce		4—40
Pine		22—40

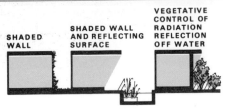

SHADED WALL   SHADED WALL AND REFLECTING SURFACE   VEGETATIVE CONTROL OF RADIATION REFLECTION OFF WATER

REFLECTED RADIATION CONTROL

the daytime temperature, but also warming the evening temperature and moderating it. More studies need to be made and information gathered to assist designers in the use of plants for solar radiation control.

WIND CONTROL

In seasonal, climatic cycles, large volumes of air are moved above the surface of the earth at varying speeds, intensities, and temperatures. Wind can control real or perceived temperature. The air (wind), if of a low velocity, may be pleasant and desirable; however, when the velocity increases, it is capable of causing great discomfort and even destruction to life and property. The flow of air is caused by and related to a number of climatic factors. Discussion of wind causes cannot be separated when considering climatic factors.

Wind may be intercepted, diverted, or lessened by obstructions such as buildings, walls, fences, earth forms, or plants. Most of the information concerning wind control was gathered in the shelterbelt studies conducted in the 1930's on the Great Plains. This data gives some general guidance to the designer using plants for wind control.

Windflow

Three types of windflow, or airflow—all moving in the same direction—are:

☐ **Laminar Airflow** — layers or streams of air flowing one on top of another. (This occurs fairly regularly, and is predictable.)

☐ **Turbulent Airflow** — air masses moving in the same direction, but in a random pattern. (Velocity of this type of airflow is unpredictable, and is, therefore, difficult to understand or control.)

☐ **Separated Airflow** — layers of air varying in momentum. (Where a separation between layers occurs, turbulence may be found.)

Changes from laminar to turbulent flow are governed by turbulence within the airstream and roughness of the surface over which it is flowing. Surfaces of buildings will always produce turbulent airflow, and separation occurs when air flows around sharp corners. When air is moving, it exerts a pressure against any surface that tends to inhibit its flow.

It is generally assumed that air has a viscosity coefficient of 0.

This means that air flows freely. Force and turbulence are produced between layers of flowing air whenever a blocking element is introduced. If the element is "streamlined," the air usually flows around it with a speed-up in the boundary layer of air next to it. The boundary layer of air generally follows the contours of the streamline shape and a minimum of turbulence occurs between layers. If the element is "bluff" (or not streamlined), then the boundary layer cannot follow the contours of the element; a separation of airflow occurs and the force between the boundary layer and the other air layers becomes greater. Turbulence is likely to occur around a bluff body.

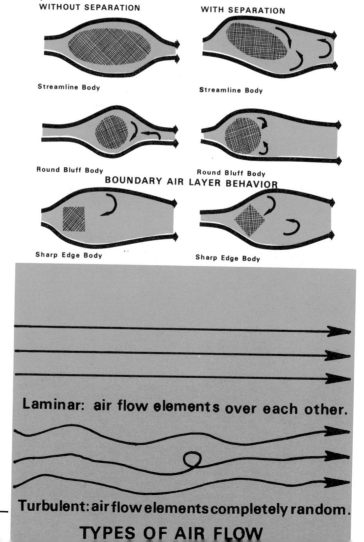

WITHOUT SEPARATION   WITH SEPARATION

Streamline Body   Streamline Body

Round Bluff Body   Round Bluff Body

BOUNDARY AIR LAYER BEHAVIOR

Sharp Edge Body   Sharp Edge Body

Laminar: air flow elements over each other.

Turbulent: air flow elements completely random.

TYPES OF AIR FLOW

Unhindered, moving wind generally flows in parallel layers. Wherever the wind flows over a streamlined surface or over a bluff body, the boundary layer of air generally speeds up, creating a low pressure area between the boundary layer and the surface of the element. The low pressure area will either cause the element to move, or attempt to pull the boundary layers of air back to its original position. When a barrier is introduced into an airstream, the wind responds by flowing around or through the barrier, eventually returning to its original flow pattern. The greater the wind velocity, the greater the pressure differential on the leeward side of the barrier, and the quicker the wind returns to its original flow pattern, lessening the area of the wake, or the protected area to the leeside of the barrier.

The weather on the lee slope of a hill is usually quieter than on the weather slope; however, this may be reversed if the weather slope is steeper than the lee slope. Where the boundary layer of air is compressed as it passes over a ridge, wind speed is usually 20 percent greater on the top of a ridge than on the slopes.

A pierced screen allowing some wind to penetrate through it creates less pressure differential, providing a larger wake on the lee side of the screen. A tree without foliage acts as an incomplete barrier, with some modifying effect on wind.

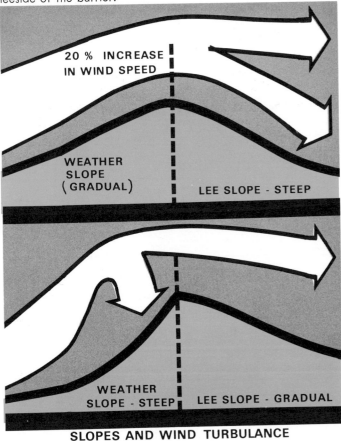

SLOPES AND WIND TURBULANCE

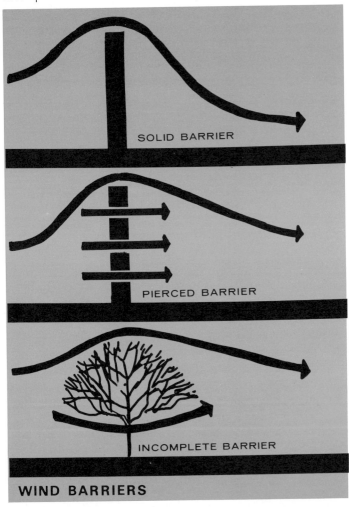

WIND BARRIERS

Plants Control Wind

Basically, plants control wind by obstruction, guidance, deflection, and filtration. The differentiation is not only one of the degree of effectiveness of plants, but of the techniques of placing plants. A number of references are available which refer to the ways in which plants control wind and their effectiveness in doing so. However, it must be remembered that plants as natural elements are not always absolutely predictable in their size, shape, and growth rate, and consequently in their absolute effectiveness.

Obstruction with trees, as with all other barriers, reduces windspeed by increasing the resistance to windflow. Coniferous and deciduous trees and shrubs used individually or in combination affect air movement.

Plants may be used in conjunction with landforms and architectural materials to alter the airflow over the landscape, and around or through buildings.

Guidance of wind is the subject of a number of studies on the placement of plants adjacent to buildings to enhance natural ventilation. The studies conducted by Robert F. White, landscape architect on the staff of the Texas Engineering Experiment Station, were primarily concerned with the wind control aspects of planting in relation to architecture to provide natural ventilation in warm areas of the world. White's research in-

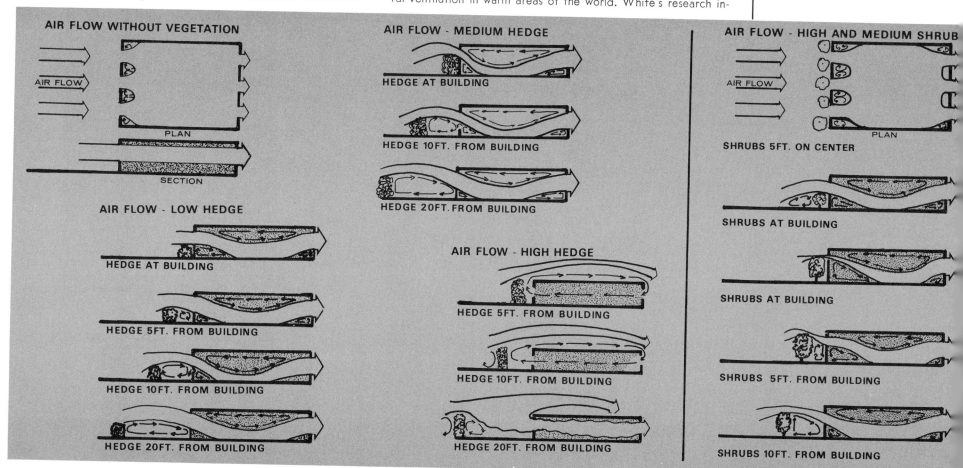

AIR FLOW WITHOUT VEGETATION

AIR FLOW

PLAN

SECTION

AIR FLOW - LOW HEDGE

HEDGE AT BUILDING

HEDGE 5 FT. FROM BUILDING

HEDGE 10 FT. FROM BUILDING

HEDGE 20 FT. FROM BUILDING

AIR FLOW - MEDIUM HEDGE

HEDGE AT BUILDING

HEDGE 10 FT. FROM BUILDING

HEDGE 20 FT. FROM BUILDING

AIR FLOW - HIGH HEDGE

HEDGE 5 FT. FROM BUILDING

HEDGE 10 FT. FROM BUILDING

HEDGE 20 FT. FROM BUILDING

AIR FLOW - HIGH AND MEDIUM SHRUB

AIR FLOW

PLAN

SHRUBS 5 FT. ON CENTER

SHRUBS AT BUILDING

SHRUBS AT BUILDING

SHRUBS 5 FT. FROM BUILDING

SHRUBS 10 FT. FROM BUILDING

dicated that: "(1) Planting can materially affect the movement of air through and about buildings, (2) Dependent on the way it is used, planting may either augment or reduce the natural airflow through the building, (3) Planting may cause actual change of direction of airflow within the building, (4) Planting on the lee side of buildings has little or no effect on the movement of air through the building, unless it is in such a position that it obstructs the outlet openings." [5] The accompanying illustrations indicate air flow around and through a number of plants and building configurations.

[5]Robert F. White, *Effects of Landscape Development on the Natural Ventilation of Buildings and Their Adjacent Areas*, Texas Engineering Experiment Station, Research Report 45 (Austin, 1945). College Station, Texas, p. 24.

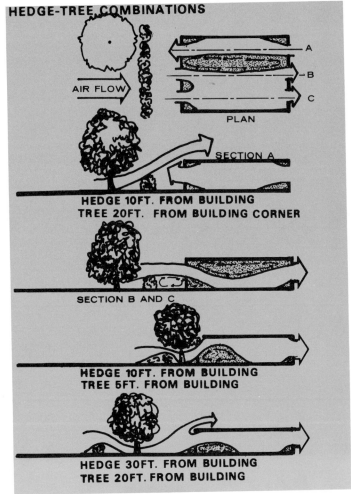

When any bluff, non-streamlined barrier is introduced into an airflow, a pressure eddy is formed immediately in front of, and a suction eddy is created immediately leeward of the barrier. Beyond the barrier a turbulent wake is created. Wind is controlled for a distance of from two to five times the height of a barrier in front of a wind obstruction, and from 10 to 15 times the height leeward of such a barrier.

Deflection of wind over trees or shrubs is another method of wind control. Plants of varying heights, widths, species, and composition, planted either individually or in rows, have varying degrees of effect on wind deflection.

For example, coniferous evergreens that branch to the ground are generally the most effective year-round plants for wind control; and deciduous shrubs and trees, when in leaf, are most effective in summer. Wind velocity is cut from 15 to 25 percent of the open field velocity directly leeward of a dense screen planting, such as spruce or fir, while a loose barrier of lombardy poplar reduces leeward wind velocity to 60 percent of its open field velocity. Wind velocity is cut from 12 to 3 miles per hour for a distance of 40 feet leeward of a 20-foot Austrian pine.

Filtration of wind, passing under or through plants, is a method of control. There are instances where it may be desirable to speed up or slow down wind.

Robert F. White, in his studies at the Texas Engineering Experiment Station, concludes that the foliage mass of a tree serves as a direct block to passage of air; and that the speed of the air movement directly beneath a tree is measurably increased over speeds measured at the same height on its lee and windward side.[6]

[6] White, p. 25.

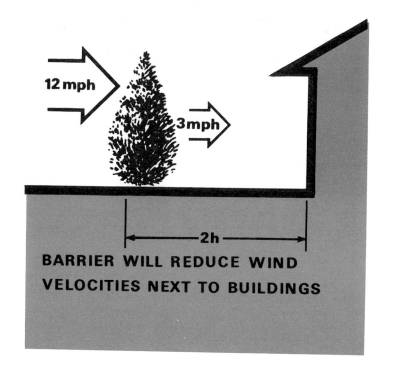

12 mph **3mph**

2h

BARRIER WILL REDUCE WIND VELOCITIES NEXT TO BUILDINGS

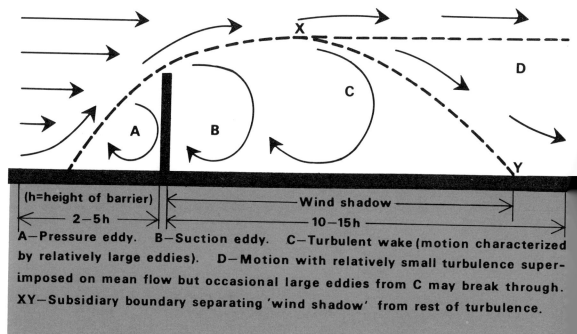

(h=height of barrier) — Wind shadow —
2—5h   10—15h

A—Pressure eddy. **B**—Suction eddy. **C**—Turbulent wake (motion characterized by relatively large eddies). **D**—Motion with relatively small turbulence superimposed on mean flow but occasional large eddies from C may break through. **XY**—Subsidiary boundary separating 'wind shadow' from rest of turbulence.

Shelter Belts

Studies have shown that shelterbelts and windbreaks are most effective when placed perpendicular to the prevailing winds. Wind velocity may be reduced by 50 percent for a distance of from 10 to 20 times the tree height downwind of a shelterbelt, and the degree of protection and wind reduction depend upon the height, width, and penetrability of the plants used.

Near a moderately dense shelterbelt, at the end of the windbreak, wind speed is increased more than 10 percent of the open field velocity prior to its interception. The leeward sheltered zone is not confined within lines drawn perpendicular to the ends of the barrier, but is broader than the length of the barrier.

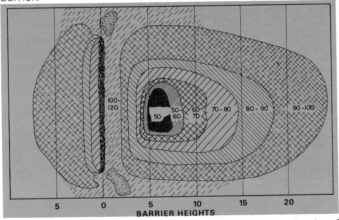

Wind speed is also affected within or on the windward side of a windbreak. For example, the wind speed is reduced for a distance of 100 yards on the windward or front side of a 30-foot-high shelterbelt, and is reduced for a distance of 300 yards downwind or behind the shelterbelt.

Partially penetrable windbreaks have different effects on windflow than do dense windbreaks. Wind velocities immediately to the leeward of any windbreak are directly affected by the type of material used or kinds of plants used.

The more penetrable the windbreak is, the longer the distance behind the windbreak protection extends. Some wind, in passing through a penetrable windbreak, retains some of its laminar flow characteristics at a reduced velocity, thus inhibiting turbulence behind it.

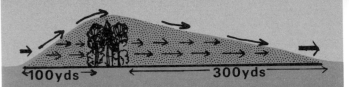

A 30ft. high shelterbelt affects wind speed for 100yds. in front of the trees and 300yds. down wind.

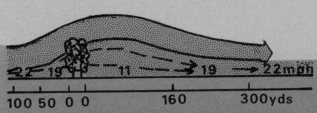

Effect of moderately penetrable windbreaks on wind.

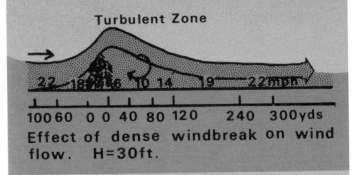

Effect of dense windbreak on wind flow. H=30ft.

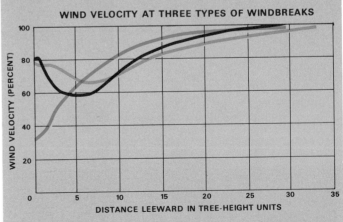

WIND VELOCITY AT THREE TYPES OF WINDBREAKS

— Board barrier 33% solid (16 feet high)
— Thin cottonwood belt (65 feet high)
— Dense ash belt (40 feet high)

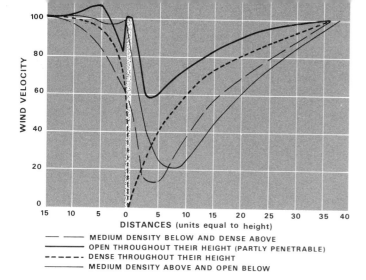

MEDIUM DENSITY BELOW AND DENSE ABOVE
— OPEN THROUGHOUT THEIR HEIGHT (PARTLY PENETRABLE)
- - - - DENSE THROUGHOUT THEIR HEIGHT
— MEDIUM DENSITY ABOVE AND OPEN BELOW

Russian scientists have conducted a number of significant studies showing the relative wind velocities in the vicinity of their shelterbelts. One study, for example, charted the effectiveness of windbreaks on the steppes of central Russia.

The accompanying illustration shows the effectiveness of open, medium dense, and dense shelterbelts in reducing wind velocities.

Two other studies on the influence of forest cover on wind movement are also illustrated. The average daily wind movement, 15 feet above the ground, inside and outside a maple-beech forest, indicates the relative effectiveness of deciduous woods to control wind throughout the year. The influence on the wind profile in an oak forest changes as the foliage emerges.

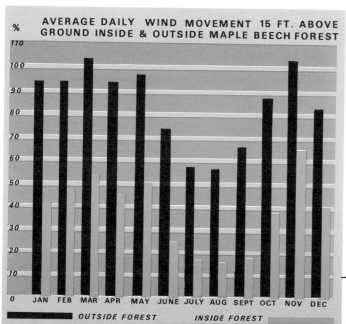

AVERAGE DAILY WIND MOVEMENT 15 FT. ABOVE GROUND INSIDE & OUTSIDE MAPLE BEECH FOREST

OUTSIDE FOREST   INSIDE FOREST

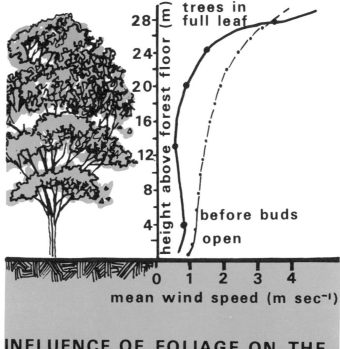

INFLUENCE OF FOLIAGE ON THE WIND PROFILE IN AN OAK FOREST

The measurement of the wind velocity differs, depending on the height at which it is recorded. The ground and the rough objects upon it slow the wind velocity near the ground surface. Rough surfaces introduced into the windstream reduce its velocity. This concept is presented in the accompanying illustration.

HEIGHT   Zone of wind reduction on the leeward and windward side of a barrier are largely dependent upon the height of the barrier. The taller the trees, the more rows of trees are required for protection. With an increase in height of the trees, shelterbelts become more open. Instead of reducing the wind, avenues of trees open at the bottom increase wind speed, as the air stream is forced beneath the tree canopy and through the tree trunks.

According to N. M. Gorshenin (1934), the influence that trees have on reducing wind velocity extends from 30 to 40 times the height of the trees leeward of the windbreak, and the sharpest reduction in wind velocity extends from 10 to 15 times the height of the trees.[7] Commenting on this same subject, B. I. Logginov (1941) stated that the maximum shelter from the wind is obtained at three to five times the height on the leeward side of trees.[8] According to H. Iizuka in 1950, wind velocities recorded, behind an artificial windbreak in Japan at distances of 10, 20, and 30 times the height of the windbreak, were respectively 66.44, 69.33, and 77.44 percent of the open wind speed.[9]

[7]N. M. Gorshenin, *Principles of Shelterbelt Layout on Arable Slopes*, U.S.S.R. All-Union Institute of Forest Culture and Forest Melioration Excerpts (Moscow, 1934), p. 73 (In Russian), U.S. Forest Service Translation No. 64, 1946, p. 49 (In English).

[8]B. I. Logginov, *Principles of Field Protective Forestation*, All-Union Academy of Agricultural Science Translations, v. 3 (Moscow, 1941), p. 28. (In Russian, English title).

[9]H. Iizuka, "On the Width of Shelterbelts," *Forestry Experimental Station*, Bulletin 56 (Meguro, 1952), p. 23. (In Japanese, English summary).

[10]Y. A. Smal'ko, "Range of Wind Sheltering in Forests Strips of Different Structures," Izvestiya AN SSSR, *geographic series* 5 (1954), p. 5.

[11]N. P. Woodruff and A. W. Zingg, "Wind Tunnel Studies of Shelterbelt Models," *Journal of Forestry*, v. 51 (1953), pp. 173-178.

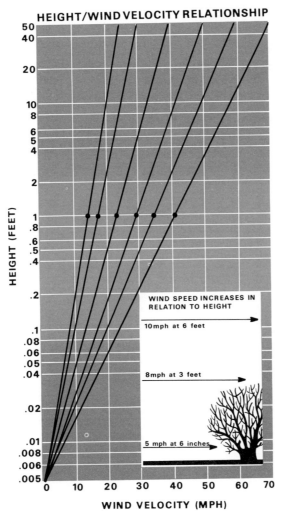

HEIGHT/WIND VELOCITY RELATIONSHIP

WIND SPEED INCREASES IN RELATION TO HEIGHT

10mph at 6 feet

8mph at 3 feet

5 mph at 6 inches

HEIGHT (FEET)

WIND VELOCITY (MPH)

WIDTH The field of effectiveness of a shelterbelt depends primarily on the height and penetrability of the shelterbelt. Width of the planting is of secondary importance only insofar as it affects the degree of penetrability. The width of the windbreak has a negligible influence on reducing wind velocity at its leeward edge, but can cause notable variation on the microclimate within the sheltered area. With a wide shelterbelt or forest, the maximum reduction in the velocity of the wind occurs within the area of the shelterbelt or forest itself. Therefore, the wide shelterbelt or forest block actually consumes its own shelter to the extent that the wind velocity is reduced within the shelter itself.

According to Smal'ko (1954), temperature stratification influences wind velocities in a tree strip of dense structure. The distance on the leeward to which it will affect the wind by reducing its velocity, varies accordingly from 18 to 37 times the height of the windscreen, depending upon temperature stratification.[10]

The accompanying diagrams, which show the flow of wind over a forest block and a narrow shelterbelt, illustrate the influence the width of a windbreak has on reducing flow.

An irregular windbreak, such as the tops of a picket fence, is more effective than a uniform one in breaking up a portion of the airstream deflected over it. A mixture of species and sizes of plants within the windbreak, therefore, produces a rough upper surface and is more effective in controlling wind.

PENETRABILITY Wind tunnel studies indicate the relative effectiveness of rows of trees within a shelterbelt. These studies by N. P. Woodruff and A. W. Zingg, in 1953, were made with models of five, seven, and 10 rows.[11] Relative wind velocities were recorded at the ground surface, at intermediate zones, and extending to three times the height of the tallest trees; and are illustrated on the accompanying charts. The order of effectiveness as windbreaks for the different designs was found to be designs C, F, B, E, D, A. The models were also studied to determine which would provide the best surface protection against wind erosion. The order of effectiveness for erosion protection was found to be designs C, A, B, D, E, F. These results should be accepted with some reservations since live trees cannot be simulated accurately on a scale model; however, they do provide the designers with some insight into the use of penetrable windbreaks to control wind.

Configurations of windflow over windbreaks were studied in the hydraulics laboratory wind tunnel at the University of Wisconsin in 1954 and 1964. Findings revealed that when a windbreak is completely impenetrable, practically the entire wind force is deflected upward, over the barrier. Pressure behind the barrier is low because the wind does not pass through the barrier, causing a suction effect and forcing the air currents above the windbreaks downward. Shelterbelts with a cross section resembling a pitched roof are less effective in blocking winds than with vertical edges.

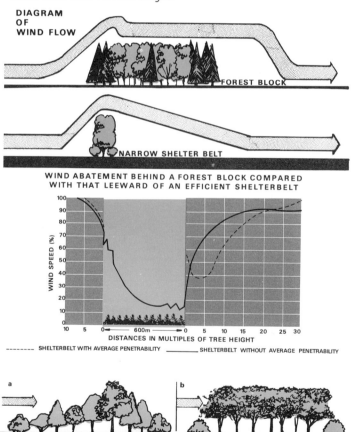

DIAGRAM OF WIND FLOW

FOREST BLOCK

NARROW SHELTER BELT

WIND ABATEMENT BEHIND A FOREST BLOCK COMPARED WITH THAT LEEWARD OF AN EFFICIENT SHELTERBELT

DISTANCES IN MULTIPLES OF TREE HEIGHT

-------- SHELTERBELT WITH AVERAGE PENETRABILITY _____ SHELTERBELT WITHOUT AVERAGE PENETRABILITY

Belts with a pitched-roof (cross section a) are less effective in halting winds than belts with more or less vertical edges.

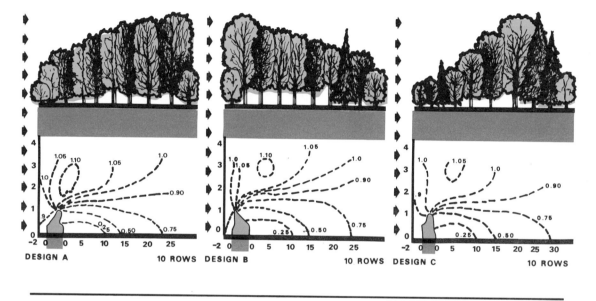

DESIGN A 10 ROWS DESIGN B 10 ROWS DESIGN C 10 ROWS

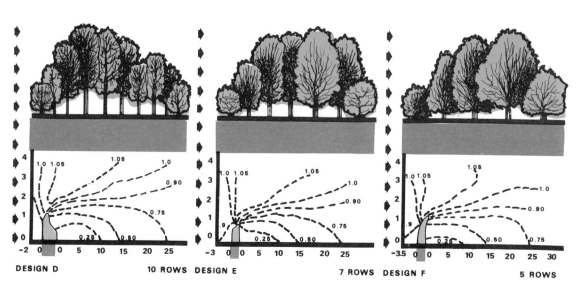

DESIGN D 10 ROWS DESIGN E 7 ROWS DESIGN F 5 ROWS

Panfilov's studies (1936) list the types of windbreaks as follows: windbreaks open throughout their height (partly penetrable to wind); windbreaks dense throughout their height (impenetrable to wind); windbreaks of medium density (slightly penetrable); windbreaks of medium density below and high density above (slightly penetrable); and windbreaks of medium density above and open below. He indicates that wind turbulence behind the windbreak increases with the density of the belt.[12] Although it may provide a greater degree of shelter from the wind on the leeward, a dense shelterbelt provides a restricted zone of effective shelter downwind. A penetrable shelterbelt has a lower percentage of actual wind reduction near the screen; but the overall effects extend a greater distance beyond. The effect of suction immediately behind the penetrable shelterbelt is less than that of a dense shelterbelt; and the acceleration of the wind back to its original force is more gradual behind a penetrable shelterbelt.

The optimum density for a shelterbelt is about 50 to 60 percent. This means that the leaves, branches, twigs, and trunks should cover 60 percent of the frontal area of the belt. With this density, narrow belts will afford as much shelter as wider belts of the same overall penetrability.

Wind-speed effects, leeward of a 30-foot-high shelterbelt of different densities, are shown in these illustrations.

Factors of penetrability and patterns of wind abatement in the vicinity of shelterbelts of different densities are also shown.

A diagram by Werner von Nageli, showing the effects of a 42-foot-wide [13] avenue of 72-foot poplar trees, spaced 21 feet apart and bare of branches for the first 25 feet, also indicates that wind accelerates under open-avenue belts, and reduces their value as wind barriers.

An accompanying chart illustrates the differences between open and closed wind barriers, based on the percent of open-field wind velocity.

In selecting plants for a windbreak and in the design of the windbreak configuration, the designer should be aware of these effects.

[12] Y. Panfilov, "A Contribution to the Problem of the Effect of the Shelterbelts on Wind Velocity on Steep Slopes, *Sovetska Agronomiska*, v. 1 (1940), pp. 11-17. (In Russian, English title).

[13] Werner von Nageli, *Uber die Windverhältnisse im Bereich gestaffelter Windschutzreifen*, v. 23, p. 14.

WIND SPEED (%) — HEIGHTS (FT)
OPEN - - - - - — DENSE — - - - - - MODERATE DENSE
VERY OPEN ——— — VERY DENSE

WIND SPEED AS SHELTERBELT IS THINNED						
NUMBER REMOVED FROM EACH SIX PLANTS IN A ROW	DISTANCE FROM SHELTERBELT (h=height of shelterbelt)					
	-2.5h	0.5h	2.5h	5.0h	7.5h	10.0h
	Wind Speed Percentage of Open Wind					
0	93	75	56	29	53	74
2	91	72	60	38	60	69
4	83	90	78	69	78	76
5	97	96	98	93	96	95
6	100	100	100	100	100	100

WIND REDUCTION TO LEEWARD OF 30 FT HIGH SHELTERBELTS OF DIFFERENT DENSITY				
	PERCENTAGE WIND SPEED REDUCTION			
Density of belt	first 50 yards	first 100 yards	first 150 yards	first 300 yards
Very open	18	24	25	18
Open	54	46	37	20
Medium	60	56	48	28
Dense	66	55	44	25
Very dense	66	48	37	20

WIND SPEEDS NEAR 30-FT.-HIGH SHELTERBELTS OF DIFFERENT DENSITY												
Density of belt	At Distances to Windward of Belt (yards)			Within the Belt	At Distances to Leeward of the Belt (yards)							
	100	50	0	0	20	50	100	150	200	250	300	
	Wind Speed as a Percentage of the Unobstructed Wind											
Very open	100	98	94	96	102	80	72	69	74	86	97	100
Open	100	96	70	75	60	40	48	75	87	95	99	100
Medium	100	96	65	62	55	37	36	60	77	89	95	100
Dense	100	96	55		40	27	42	70	86	94	97	100
Very dense	100	95	55		15	27	58	82	91	96	99	100

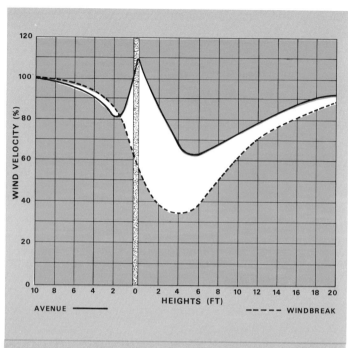

WIND VELOCITY (%)

AVENUE ——— WINDBREAK - - - -

HEIGHTS (FT)

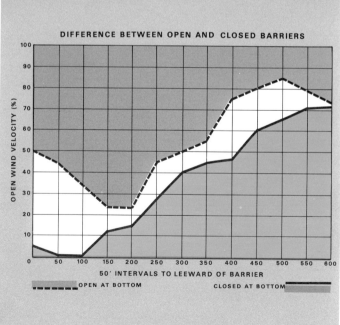

DIFFERENCE BETWEEN OPEN AND CLOSED BARRIERS

OPEN WIND VELOCITY (%)

50' INTERVALS TO LEEWARD OF BARRIER

OPEN AT BOTTOM - - - -   CLOSED AT BOTTOM ———

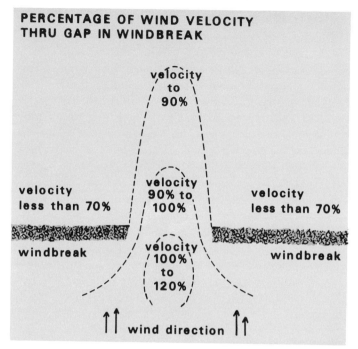

PERCENTAGE OF WIND VELOCITY THRU GAP IN WINDBREAK

velocity to 90%

velocity less than 70%   velocity 90% to 100%   velocity less than 70%

windbreak   velocity 100% to 120%   windbreak

wind direction

LENGTH Research shows that the lines of equal wind velocity (isotacks) have a tendency to deviate toward the center of the barrier in the field of protection afforded by windbreaks, and to adapt courses parallel to it. An extension of the barrier changes nothing except that the zones of isotacks parallel to it are widened. The most efficient ratio of height to length for windbreaks is 1:11.5. According to Werner von Nageli, this ratio produces the greatest possible shelter effect, at least near the center of the shelterbelt. [14] As a result of the air current sweeping around the shelterbelts, increased wind velocity, higher than that found in the open field, occurs at both ends of windbreaks. According to Kreutz (1950), smoke experiments have confirmed this.[15]

Frequent gaps in a system of shelterbelts, particularly where belts intersect one another with a gap of 12-meter widths (40 feet), are advocated by the Russian scientists. According to one study, as a zone of wind-velocity increase develops within the gap, there is practically no lateral extension of this "draught" zone, and at a short distance from the gap the wind abatement is normal. Findings also were made by J. van Eimern

[14] Werner von Nageli, *Untersuchungen uber die Windverhältnisse im Bereich von Schilfrohrwanden*, v. 29 (Ebenda, 1953), p. 82.
[15] W. Kreutz, *Der Windschutz* (Dortmund, 1952), p. 83.

in 1951, who measured a wind velocity of 3.6 meters per second in the open and a wind velocity of 4.5 meters per second within the gaps between shelterbelts.[16]

Parallel shelterbelts, spaced widely apart, have no cumulative effect on reducing wind velocity. According to Carlos G. Bates, however, each shelterbelt has a larger coherent mass of stilled air within a zone of seven to 12 times the height of that belt, stretching laterally from the leeward edge of it, creating some small degree of protection.[17] A series of shelterbelts, spaced closer than five times their height, have some cumulative effect. It would appear that when the distances between two shelterbelts is less than 30 times their height, the velocity of the wind between the two never reaches the velocity of the free wind; but scientific evidence does not substantiate this.

A windbreak has a protective effect for a distance equal to the height of the barrier, and leeward of it. If the barrier is a dense planting, it will remain relatively stable, and the percentage value of minimum wind velocity will remain relatively unchanged.

In a penetrable windbreak, the protective effect is somewhat less next to the barrier and is felt at a distance equal to its height, and the zone of overall protection is more pronounced. The increased shelter effect with increased free wind velocity has been mentioned frequently. One study indicates that wind measurements made during a period of 30 years, demonstrated that a spruce belt reduces the wind velocity by 30 percent and up to 47 percent during heavy gales (Geiger, 1931). The relative shelter effect behind a barrier of rigid form remains more or less the same for varying speeds of wind. However, when the windbreak changes its form according to wind pressure, as illustrated by trees bending and swaying, the penetrability and vertical structure of it are affected, and the zone of reduced velocity is decreased. A row of trees, being somewhat elastic, will change its form according to the prevailing wind speed, thereby affecting the resistance to the wind and the degree of penetrability (Bates). The percentage of velocity reduction and the zone of quieter air increase as the wind becomes stronger and the center of the quieter air tends to move farther away from the windbreak on the leeward side.

A moderately penetrable shelterbelt becomes more impenetra-

ble in high winds. Similarly, a belt too sparse to give protection in light winds affords a greater degree of shelter as the wind velocity increases.

According to M. Jensen, sheltering efficiency of a treebelt is reduced when the wind passes over a very rough surface before it strikes the belt.[18] The character of wind is very important in determining the type, size, and characteristics of the windbreak (trees) required.

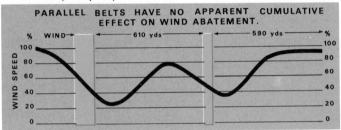

WIND VELOCITY PROFILES

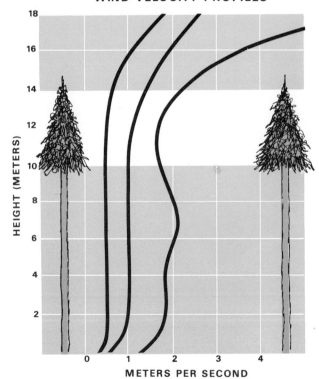

[16]J. van Eimern, "Kleineklimatische Geländeaufnahme in Quickbom/Holstein," *Annalen der Meteorologie*, v. 4 (1951), pp. 259-269.

[17]Carlos G. Bates, "The Windbreak as a Farm Asset," *Farmers Bulletin*, no. 1405 (1944), p. 4.

[18]M. Jensen, *Shelter Effect: Investigations into the Aerodynamics of Shelter and Its Effects on Climate and Crops* (Copenhagen, 1954), p. 38.

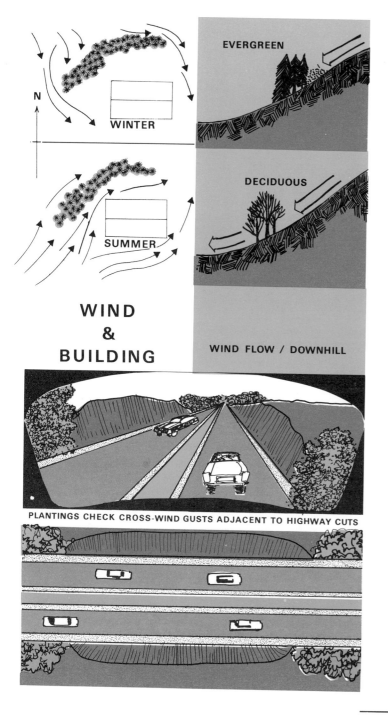

WIND & BUILDING

EVERGREEN

DECIDUOUS

WIND FLOW / DOWNHILL

PLANTINGS CHECK CROSS-WIND GUSTS ADJACENT TO HIGHWAY CUTS

Intermediate Control

Prevailing winds may change direction seasonally; therefore, plants used should be of the type best suited for controlling winds from all directions. For instance, a dense coniferous windbreak of pyramidal arborvitae on the northwest side of a structure may protect it from harsh winter winds, and yet direct summer breezes around it. Not only may wind be slowed down or deflected for preserving a degree of warmth, it may also provide a degree of coolness by acceleration and channeling through an opening in a planting, or be guided in a desired direction by the angle of the planting. The advantageous use of plants to control the wind can reduce the cost of interior heating and cooling.

Cooler winds flow downhill at night. Dense evergreen plants placed on a slope, trap and hold cold wind flow upwind, thus creating cool spaces. Deciduous or "loose" plants create cool spaces on the downwind side by filtering the air.

Wind gusts may be effectively controlled by planting along highways, to break the force of wind gusts blowing against the sides of automobiles. According to J. M. Caborn:

There are pockets along many highways, particularly when emerging from road cuts, where furious gusts can catch a car broadside and have a disconcerting effect on the driver—even a dangerous one at high speeds. Not all these hazardous spots could be improved by shelterbelts, particularly in a wild broken country . . . but some could.[19]

Ventilation

All functional uses of plant material are interconnected; therefore it is difficult and artificial to attempt to separate one use from another. Dr. Wilfrid Bach and Dr. Edward Mathews, in a paper on "The Importance of Green Areas in Urban Planning" state in regard to ventilation in urban areas:

Wind is one of the most important climatic elements in urban planning, since dispersion of air pollution and human comfort are largely dependent on it. Winds that are too strong cause the funnel effect in our canyon-like streets. This may locally lead to high air pollution potential through lifted street dust and strong wind fumigation from elevated sources. Winds which are too light may lead to stagnation conditions which may also produce high air pollution potential and in summer muggy conditions.

The ideal ventilation system would prevent the funnelling effect but favor the country breeze, i.e., wind blowing from relatively cleaner and cooler country, suburban, or green areas. This could be achieved by a properly spaced system of green areas cutting through the entire built-up area.[20]

PRECIPITATION CONTROL

Precipitation in all forms—rain, fog, dew, snow, sleet, and hail

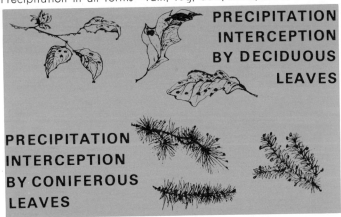

PRECIPITATION INTERCEPTION BY DECIDUOUS LEAVES

PRECIPITATION INTERCEPTION BY CONIFEROUS LEAVES

—is intercepted and controlled to some degree by plants. Leaves, needles, twigs, branches, trunks, and bark—all catch, entrap, hold, and filter precipitation. Therefore, radiation, precipitation and humidity, around, through, and under plants—modify temperature to the extent that it is sensed by the human in the environment.

The purpose of this section is to discuss how plants can be used to control precipitation as one element of climate modification.

Plants And Rain

INTERCEPTION   Some precipitation that falls on a tree does not reach the ground. The amount of rainfall which reaches the ground varies not only according to the species of the trees, but also according to the particular zone under the tree canopy. Some studies have indicated that only 60 percent of the rain falling on a pine forest canopy reaches the ground, and 80 percent of the rain falling on a hardwood forest canopy reaches the ground. H. W. Beale (1934), H. F. Linskens (1951), and J. D. Ovington (1954),[21] demonstrated the difference in the quantity of rainfall reaching the ground under softwoods (conifers) and hardwoods. The annual average of water reaching the ground is greater under hardwoods than conifers. The reasons are because softwoods have leaves with a greater number of sharp angles and trap water droplets in their numerous cavities; they absorb moisture resulting from precipitation and transpiration.

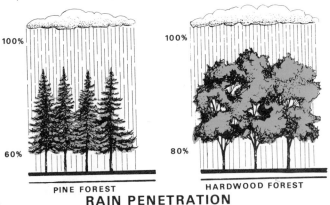

PINE FOREST   HARDWOOD FOREST
RAIN PENETRATION

[19]J. M. Caborn, *Windbreaks and Shelterbelts* (London, 1965), p. 133.

[20]Wilfrid Bach and Edward Mathews, "The Importance of Green Acres in Urban Planning," Paper prepared for Bioclimatology and Environmental Health Workshop, Public Health Service, U.S. Department of Health, Education, and Welfare, Cincinnati, July 14-16, 1969.

[21]Specific citations follow further references to each individual.

Beale (1934) conducted an experiment which showed variations in the percentage of rainfall reaching the ground under a tree in different locations.[22]

The percentage of precipitation actually reaching the ground under particular parts of various species of trees was measured by Linskens (1951).[23]

The illustrations indicate the percentage of precipitation in the form of rain and snow reaching the ground under beech, apple, oak, maple, and conifers.

INTENSITY OF RAINFALL   The intensity of the rainfall is a key factor in the ability of plants to control precipitation. In light rain softwoods have a greater water retention ability than do hardwoods.

Ovington (1954) said that in light rainfall, conifers retain as much as five times the quantity of water as that intercepted and retained by broad-leafed trees.[24] After a long rain shower the tree canopies and the boles in the branches and trunks become saturated, and an appreciable quantity of water runs down into the soil.

The amount of water reaching the ground is dependent upon the tree canopy structure, rather than upon the size of the tree. The rain reaches the ground under plants in two forms: raindrops which are not intercepted and pass freely through the leaves; and the dripping of previously intercepted raindrops from the leaves and branches of the tree. The presence or absence of foliage in the hardwoods does not, with the probable exception of very light rainfall, affect the percentage of water penetrating the canopy (Ovington). One study demonstrated that the leaves were the main reason for the variations in percentage of water reaching the ground (Linskens). Another showed that the intensity of rainfall is of greater importance than the time of the year (Ovington).

The amount of rainfall which reaches the ground is influenced by the intensity and duration of the rainfall, the type of tree (coniferous or deciduous), and the structure of the tree canopy rather than the season (such as hardwoods with or without leaves).

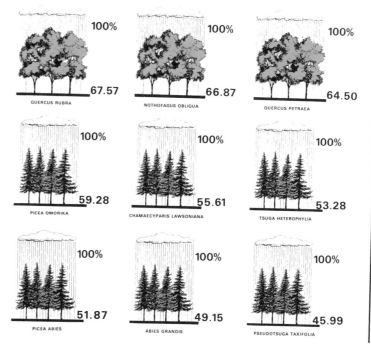

DISTRIBUTION OF PRECIPITATION UNDER TREES

BEECH   WEEPING APPLE   PYRAMIDAL OAK   MAPLE   CONIFER

TREES IN WINTER SNOW

TREES IN SUMMER RAIN

150
150-120
120-110
110-80
80-70
70-50
50
50
SITE MEASUREMENT

LARIX EUROLEPSIS   100%   69.58
QUERCUS RUBRA   100%   67.57
NOTHOFAGUS OBLIQUA   100%   66.87
QUERCUS PETRAEA   100%   64.50

THUYA PLICATA   100%   63.37
PICEA OMORIKA   100%   59.28
CHAMAECYPARIS LAWSONIANA   100%   55.61
TSUGA HETEROPHYLIA   100%   53.28

PINUS NIGRA   100%   52.12
PICEA ABIES   100%   51.87
ABIES GRANDIS   100%   49.15
PSEUDOTSUGA TAXIFOLIA   100%   45.99

[22]H. W. Beale, "The Penetration of Rainfall through Hardwood and Softwood Forest Canopy," *Ecology, v.* 15 (1934), pp. 412-415.

[23]H. F. Linskens, "Niederschlagemessungen unter verschiedenen Baukronentypen im belaubten und unbelaubten Austand," Bericht der deutschen Botanischen Gesellschaft, v. 64 (1951), pp. 215-221.

[24]J. D. Ovington, "A Comparison of Rainfall in Different Woodlands," *Forestry,* v. 27 (1954), pp. 41-43.

DISTRIBUTION OF PRECIPITATION (% OF ANNUAL AVERAGE) FALLING ON TWO STANDS OF TREES

TREE TYPE	SEASON	INTERCEPTION	TRUNK FLOW	THROUGHFALL
Fir	Summer	32.4	0.7	66.9
	Winter	26.0	0.7	73.3
Beech	Summer	16.4	16.6	67.0
	Winter	10.4	16.6	73.0

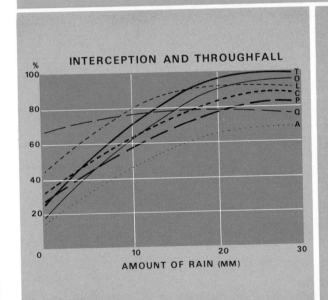

INTERCEPTION AND THROUGHFALL

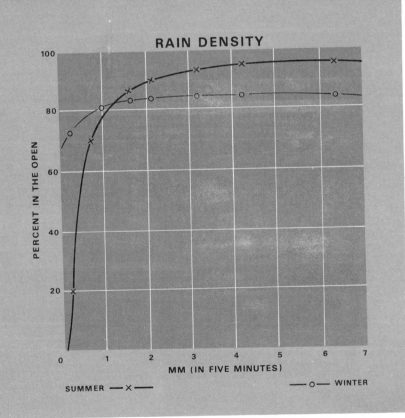

RAIN DENSITY

INTERCEPTION OF VARIOUS TYPES OF TREES						
SAPLINGS	HEIGHT IN METERS		QUANTITIES MEASURED			
TYPE OF TREE (all 22–23yr old)	Stand	Crown canopy	Through fall (%)	Trunk flow (%)	Drops (%)	Snowfall (mm)
Deciduous						
Q Quercus rubra	7.3	2.4	68–71	0.3	68	13
Coniferous						
L Larix eurolepsis	14.6	3.0	70–90	0.1	45	7
T Thuja plicata	7.6	2.1	63–65	0.1	46	1
O Picea omorica	10.1	4.0	59–61	0.2	66	0
C Chamaecyparis lawsonia	8.8	1.8	56–57	0.1	48	
P Pinus nigra	8.5	2.1	52–53	0.2	61	1
A Abies grandis	14.3	4.9	49	0.1	64	

TRANSPIRATION AND EVAPORATION Various parts of plants intercept precipitation and thus are able to modify or control climate; trees and shrubs tend to cause an increase in precipitation above them. Leaf surfaces cause excess transpiration of water from the soil through the plant into the atmosphere immediately above the plant.

Dr. John Carew of Michigan State University estimated that on a single day in summer, an acre of turf will lose about 2,400 gallons of water to transpiration and evaporation.[25]

The tree or shrub canopy serves to prevent evaporation of moisture from soil into the atmosphere. In this way, plants preserve and retain moisture in the soil. Because of these factors a diurnal temperature-humidity relationship exists.

HUMIDITY AND TEMPERATURE Because plants block and filter solar radiation, inhibit windflow, transpire water into the atmosphere, and reduce evaporation from the soil, a microclimate of controlled humidity and temperature exists under plants, particularly in a forest-like cover of plants. The relatively high humidity and low evaporation rate acts to stabilize temperature, keeping it lower than the surrounding air during the day and preventing it from dropping greatly at night. Three accompanying illustrations depict temperature-humidity relationships within a forest on a cloudy day, a clear night, and a windy day.

MOISTURE RETENTION Moisture reaching the earth through a shrub or tree canopy is retained longer than moisture falling upon exposed soil. The ability of plants to intercept precipitation and slow it down helps to control surface water runoff and resulting soil erosion. Through the addition of organic material, plants loosen and maintain the porosity of the soil, which helps it retain water. The protection from sun and wind provided by plants reduces evaporation of soil water. Therefore, large-scale plantings which entrap water and help the soil retain it, are used on watersheds above reservoirs. These plants serve several purposes. They slow down water runoff, prevent soil erosion and reservoir siltation, and reduce evaporation of soil water. This also applies in critical areas over natural underground aquifers used for water supply sources.

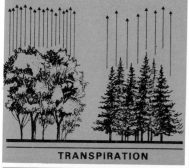

TRANSPIRATION

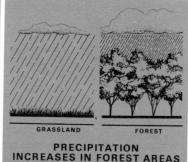

GRASSLAND FOREST
PRECIPITATION
INCREASES IN FOREST AREAS

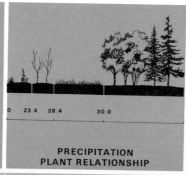

23.4 28.4 30.0

PRECIPITATION
PLANT RELATIONSHIP

GRASS
PRESERVATION OF MOISTURE

FOREST

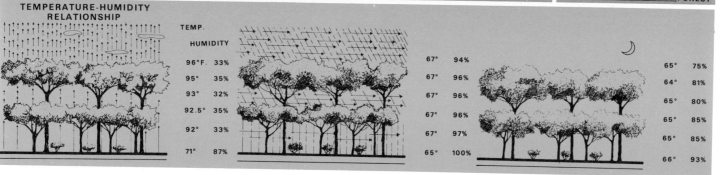

TEMPERATURE-HUMIDITY
RELATIONSHIP

TEMP.	HUMIDITY
96°F.	33%
95°	35%
93°	32%
92.5°	35%
92°	33%
71°	87%

67°	94%
67°	96%
67°	96%
67°	96%
67°	97%
65°	100%

65°	75%
64°	81%
65°	80%
65°	85%
65°	85%
66°	93%

[25]"Nature's Own Cooling System," *Nursery Business* (September-October 1970), p. 59.

Plants and Fog and Dew

Fog condenses on the needles of conifers and on the upper and lower surfaces of leaves on deciduous trees. This condensate of fog then falls to the earth as drip water from the various parts of the plant.

When the crown of a tree is covered with dew the ground below it is generally free of it. Geiger made a study of dew measurements under an isolated beech tree during a 1-month period. The results are summarized in the accompanying chart. He also refers to a comparative study of the deposition of dew upon open ground and within a young fir plantation, and notes that the greatest deposition of dew within the fir stand occurs at the crown level of the trees, while above open ground it occurs just above the ground surface. The dew on a stand of trees, on some nights, may become quite heavy and drip through and release a brief shower.[26]

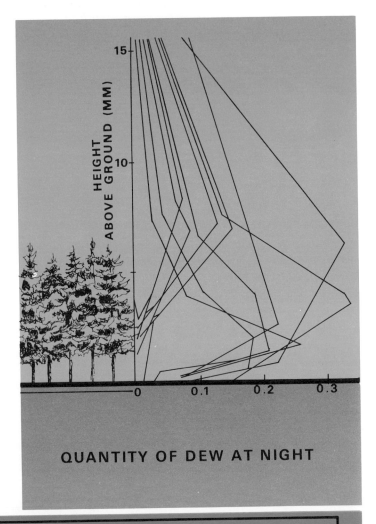

QUANTITY OF DEW AT NIGHT

PINES CONDENSE FOG

FOG DRIP WATER

DEW MEASUREMENTS UNDER AN ISOLATED BEECH						
HEIGHT ABOVE GROUND (m)	QUANTITY OF DEW (mm)		DURATION OF DEPOSITION OF DEW (hr)		DURATION OF DEW (hr)	
	Inside	Outside	Inside	Outside	Inside	Outside
14.0 (above the tree)	0.95	0.95	94	94	135	135
10.5 (under crown surface)	0.42	0.90	92	118	118	155
5.0 (in crown of beech)	0.08	0.50	47	114	62	155
1.0 (under the crown)	0.04	1.42	13	200	17	264
0.1 (under the crown)	0.05	1.42	13	268	18	334

[26]Geiger, *Climate*, p. 324.

WINDBREAKS FOR COLLECTING SNOW

ROAD

WINDBREAK DESIGNED TO TRAP SNOW ADJACENT TO A ROAD

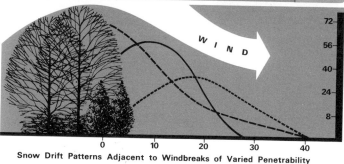

Snow Drift Patterns Adjacent to Windbreaks of Varied Penetrability

Impenetrable — — —   Semi-Penetrable ———   Penetrable ┈┈┈

Plants and Snow

Plants control snow by intercepting snowflakes, by directing wind to scour an area clean or control snowdrift location, by determining conformation and depth, by providing shade areas for snow retention and controlled melt, and by causing variations in frost depth to slow down melting.

INTERCEPTION   Plants inhibit and intercept snowflakes more than raindrops, because snowflakes are larger, travel at a lower velocity, and are not viscous. Generally, snow is held on the leaves, branches, or needles of trees. Snow is retained on the trees longer than rain; therefore, trees withhold the moisture for a longer period, allowing some to fall as large masses before melting and some to fall as it melts. This may be observed after a heavy snowfall in a forest.

DRIFT CONTROL   Plants can control the drifting of snow. As plants slow the wind velocity, snow particles are deposited in front of, among, and leeward of them. Various studies have been conducted, showing patterns, and the most effective planting configurations for controlling them.

Caborn refers to windbreaks designed for collecting snow. He feels that windbreaks should include shrubs to form snowdrifts on the windward or leeward sides of the windbreak.[27]

He refers to studies conducted in Czechoslovakia by Luncz showing the effect of snowdrift patterns, adjacent to windbreaks with different degrees of penetrability. This effect is illustrated in the accompanying chart.

Windborne snow is deposited wherever there is a local drop in wind velocity. Wind velocity is reduced wherever the airflow encounters a barrier which will project a "wind shadow" area. A great deal of effort has been directed toward understanding the pattern and distribution of snow for agricultural purposes and for the protection of transportation systems. Two ways of protecting an area against snowdrifts are snow fences and windbreaks. The fence is standardized, it gives immediate protection, and raises few objections from landowners. The main disadvantage of a snow fence is cost and yearly maintenance.

Windbreaks, with height as a prime advantage, are also important assets when there is a variation in topography. A good windbreak should filter the wind and trap the snow. Tall

[27]Caborn, *Shelterbelts*, p. 224.

trees are not sufficient to initiate drifting. They must be augmented with shrubs and ground covers. The depth of the drift and the extent of the drifting depend upon the penetrability of the plant barrier or fence. Solid fences or plantings produce drifts on both sides, while an open structure keeps the drift to the leeward side. The leeward drifts near a solid screen are generally deep, do not extend to a great length, and reach their maximum saturation point a short distance from the barrier. The leeward drifts near a penetrable screen are shallow, extend to a greater distance from the barrier, and absorb more snow. The greater the velocity of wind, the closer the drift is to the barrier itself. The optimum efficiency of a barrier is attained with a 50 percent density. A barrier with a density of approximately 50 percent and 4 feet high will initiate the formation of a drift extending up to 56 feet in length. According to Caborn in his studies in 1963, a 3-foot-high barrier results in a drift extending to 51 feet.[28]

M. Jensen showed that the length of drift is related to the height in feet of the screen in the following fashion:

$$L = \frac{36 + 5h}{K}$$

L = the length of the drift in feet
h = the height of the screen in feet
K = the function of the screen density. 1 for a 50% density, 1.28 for a 70% density.[29]

This should not be rigorously applied and a safety margin (20 feet) should be allowed for between the screen and the end of the snowdrift.

J. H. Stoeckler and E. J. Dortignac showed that narrow belts of tall trees, devoid of branches near the ground, allowed snow to sweep under the trees. The snow was deposited in thin layers on the leeside of the belt, in a band extending between 60 and 120 feet beyond the belt. The same writers reported that

[28] Caborn, *Shelterbelts*, p. 302.
[29] M. Jensen, *Shelter Effect* (Copenhagen, 1954), p. 84.

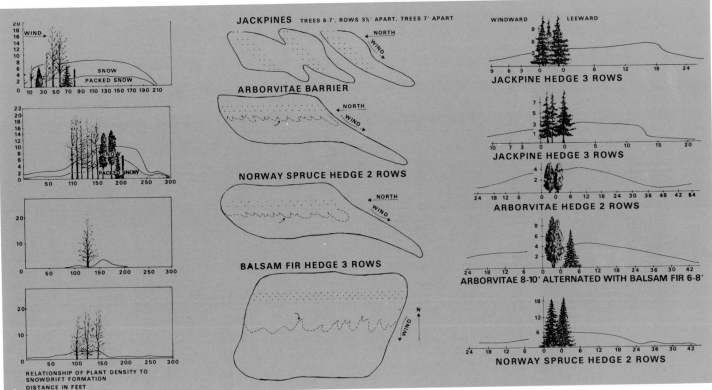

shelter-belts, with one or more dense-growing shrub rows at least 8 feet high, were very effective in trapping snow and drifts from 5 to 8 feet or more in depth, and that the snow was practically all deposited in a band from 30 to 40 feet wide on the leeside of the first row of shrubs.[30]

The effectiveness of plants in conjunction with snow drifting, is well illustrated in a quote from an article by Harold E. Olson, in the March 1963 issue of "Park Maintenance":

Where the design or location of highways cause or permit the drifting of snow, it is sometimes considered desirable to plant trees and shrubs rather than to erect and dismantle the slat-type snow fencing. This item results in an expenditure in one State of over $300,000 per annum. In this same State the cost of the removal of snow ran to $701,400—a considerable expenditure of money with no resulting betterments.

The natural barrier, or snow fence, consists of trees or shrubs planted in rows or groups in such a way as to slow down the normal velocity of the wind and cause the snow to be deposited before it reaches the traveled way. This type of snow control is best adapted to wind right-of-ways and localities where permanent snow fences may be left in place the year round. The natural barrier fits in very nicely with the modern trend toward roadside development.[31]

The accompanying charts show the effectiveness of various windbreak configurations in snow-drifting control in North Dakota.

Plants, in addition to being used to prevent snowdrifting where it is not desired, may also be used to cause snowdrifting and snow deposition desired by the operators of ski areas, toboggan runs, and other facilities which need snowfall.

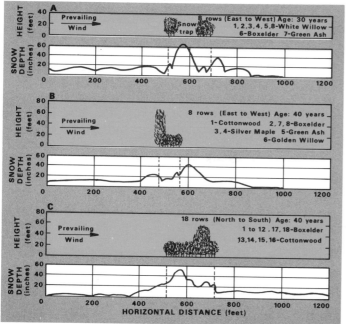

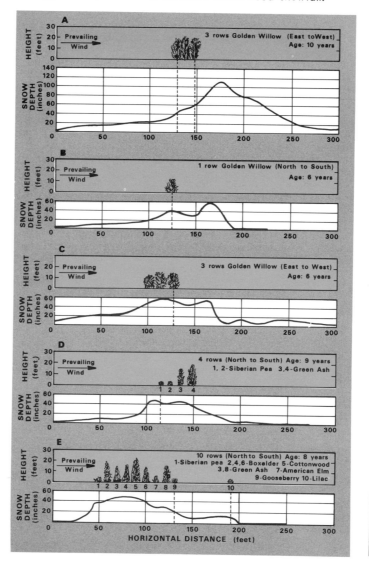

[30]J. H. Stoeckler and E. J. Dortignac, "Snowdrifts as a Factor in Growth and Longevity of Shelterbelts in the Great Plains," *Ecology*, v. 22 (1941), pp. 117-124.

[31]Harold E. Olson, "Landscape Planting for Snowdrift Control," *Park Maintenance* (March 1963), pp. 20-25.

Prudent planting greatly reduces the cost of snow removal on parking lots and other areas. As noted previously, the speed of the wind is accelerated through openings in shelterbelts, as well as at the ends of windbreak planting. This information may be utilized to provide snowfree parking lots, roadways, or walkways.

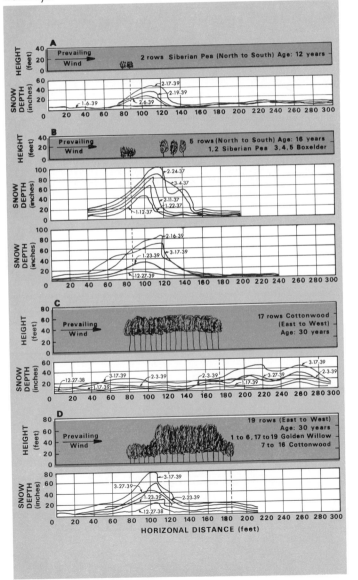

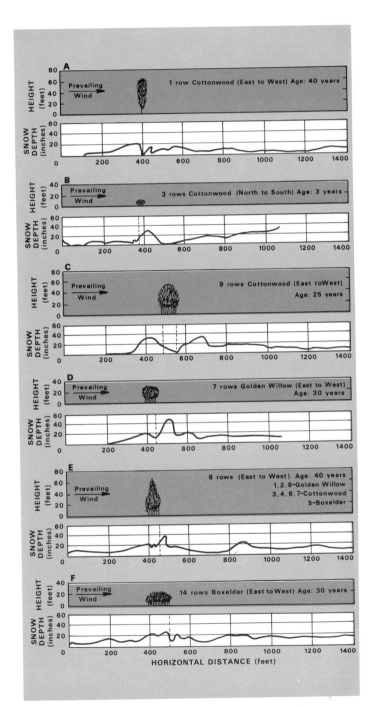

SHADING Snowfall which has drifted onto the north side of large conifers, such as spruce, fir, or pine, is shaded from the late winter sun, and lasts longer. This may be undesirable on a driveway or golf course, but is of great benefit on a ski or tobogganing hill. This also is desirable for controlling and slowing down snow melt, permitting it to enter the ground rather than run off.

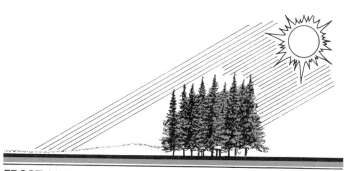

FROST LINE Undisturbed litter on the forest floor or on the ground under groups of trees enables the frost line to penetrate deeper during the colder months when freezing occurs. This makes the ground colder, ensuring that snow which falls on frozen ground will not melt rapidly. This will affect the retention of fallen snow, and it will remain in a frozen state upon the earth for a longer time. This may be desirable or undersirable, depending upon the circumstances. However, it should be recognized that plants do provide an insulating layer.

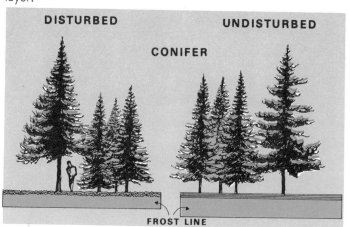

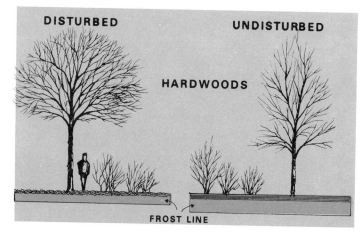

TEMPERATURE CONTROL

Temperature control is linked directly to—and is a result of—solar radiation control, wind control, and precipitation control. Plants used for temperature control have the greatest effect by moderating temperatures near the ground.

Shade and Absorption

Of the radiation that strikes a plant, very little will penetrate it, whether the radiation is direct or reflected. The shaded side has cooler temperatures than the radiated side.

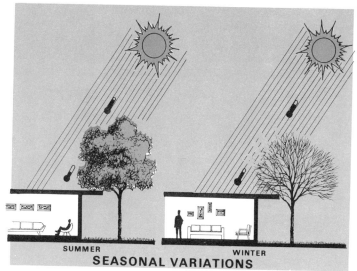

The temperature of an area may be reduced by plants even if they are not tall enough to give shade. Plants and grassy covers reduce temperatures by scattering of light and radiation and the absorption of solar radiation, and also by the evapo-transpiration process.

It is found that temperatures over grassy surfaces on sunny summer days are about 10° to 14° cooler than those of exposed soil.

Deciduous trees are good temperature control devices, in that they cool in summer and yet allow winter sun to pass through. Vines on walls or trellises are also some of nature's automatic heat control devices—cooling by evaporation and providing shade.

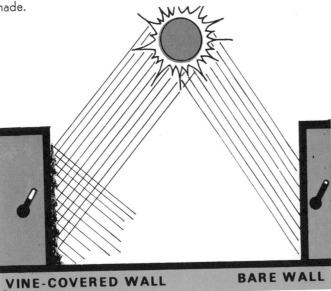

VINE-COVERED WALL   BARE WALL

Heat Transfer

Leaves absorb solar radiation, resulting in lowering the temperature in the shade of the plants. The same canopy of leaves acts to keep heat from being radiated out from under the plant, so that re-radiated heat loss during the night is reduced.

During the day the effect of shading by trees reduces the air temperature near the ground. The amount of temperature reduction depends upon the species of trees providing shade. A. Muterich showed that in a stand of beech in July, the daily

fluctuation of the air temperature at ground level is about 4.5°C.; whereas, in a stand of fir, it is about 3.9°C.; and in a stand of Scotch pine, about 3°C.[32]

On a sunny summer day the solar radiation from the sun strikes the surface of the canopy and it becomes the warmest part of the forest. Due to the absorption and reflection of heat by the canopy, the understory is cooler. Successively lower layers receive less heat and in consequence are progressively cooler. F. L. Waterhouse has observed that the highest air temperatures are usually found at the level where there is a maximum absorption of incoming radiation.[33]

At night the forest loses great quantities of heat by radiation into space. The canopy surface is the most effective radiating surface in the forest, for it is exposed directly to the sky. Heat radiated from the lower layers of the forest is trapped by the overlying strata. Because the canopy loses its heat most rapidly, it becomes the coolest part of the forest. As the air in the canopy cools it grows more dense and sinks toward the ground. In settling, this air is warmed only slightly, so that at night, the temperatures are nearly uniform from canopy to soil.

Restriction of outgoing radiation by the tree crowns, from the narrow strip along a forest margin, depends on the species of

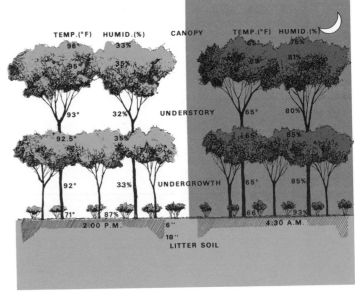

[32]A. Meterich, *Bericht über die Untersuchung der Einwirkung des Waldes auf die Menge der Niederschlage* (Neudamm, 1903), p. 32.

[33]F. L. Waterhouse, "Micrometeorological Profiles in Grass Cover in Relation to Biological Problems," *The Quarterly Journal of the Royal Meteorological Society*, v. 81 (1955), pp. 63-71

forest trees and the shape of the crowns of the trees. If the outgoing radiation is restricted, this, with the warmer air flowing outward from the trunk space under the canopy, should theoretically produce higher night temperatures on the forest margin. However, this warmer temperature may be counteracted by the downward flow of cold air from the crowns, so that the margins of plantings may also have uniform temperature from the ground to canopy (Geiger). The diurnal amplitude of temperature fluctuations within the sheltered area under plants is directly related to the range of day and night temperatures of the air surrounding the plant. On warm days and cold nights the temperature will fluctuate more than on days and nights when the temperature remains uniform.

During a rain, drops of water strike virtually every exposed surface in the forest. The water absorbs heat from surfaces that are warmer than itself; and as it drips and falls, it transfers the heat to lower, cooler surfaces. Thus temperatures are equalized and in a short time after a rain starts falling, the temperature is uniform from the canopy to forest floor litter under the plant. At the ground level, loose litter, dead leaves, and forest soil are efficient insulators on the forest floor. The ground temperature below the litter on a forest floor is subject to slight changes from day to day.

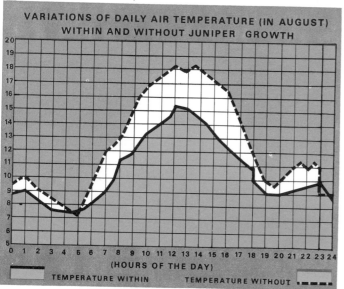

VARIATIONS OF DAILY AIR TEMPERATURE (IN AUGUST) WITHIN AND WITHOUT JUNIPER GROWTH

(HOURS OF THE DAY)

TEMPERATURE WITHIN   TEMPERATURE WITHOUT

Within soil under low plants without much litter, the temperature may fluctuate some, but it will still fluctuate less than will the soil temperature of bare ground. This is because much of the solar radiation absorbed by a barren surface during the day, heating up the soil, will be re-radiated into the atmosphere at night, warming the atmosphere and causing the soil to cool. The soil under plants absorbs little solar radiation during the day, quickly re-radiating what little heat it did absorb, thus heating the air next to the soil under the plants. Since warm air rises, a canopy of trees will tend to collect and hold warm air, retaining much of it near the ground; thus minimizing the diurnal temperature changes near the ground. The capacity of the canopy to hold the warm air is directly related to the density of the foliage. The rate of heat loss by re-radiation, retarded by plant cover, results in nocturnal temperature variations of both the soil under and air within the plant cover, with temperatures not dropping as low as the soil and air temperature of adjacent areas. Thus temperature fluctuates less widely under plant cover than where the soil is bare.

CANOPY EFFECT—NIGHT

In the absence of appreciable wind, cool soil of shaded areas absorbs heat from the air more rapidly than heat can be transmitted by convection or conduction from unshaded areas. Furthermore, the greater humidity of the air under plants increases the amount of heat needed to raise its temperature significantly. For these reasons, forests generally depress maximal air temperatures as well as maximal soil temperatures.

Air Movement

WIND Control of wind also controls temperature. Air movement affects human body cooling; it does not decrease temperature, but causes a cooling sensation due to heat loss by convection and due to increased evaporation from the body.

Trees generally reduce the wind velocity and produce a sheltered area on the leeside and to a smaller extent on the wind side of the screen. This reduction in wind velocity brings about a lowering of the rate of thermodynamic exchanges between the air layers, with the result that protection from the wind generally permits higher temperatures to prevail in the protected zones. For instance, the temperature on the leeward side of an evergreen barrier made up of plants such as white pine, eastern arborvitae, or eastern red cedar is warmer, both during the day and at night. This concept is illustrated in the accompanying diagrams.

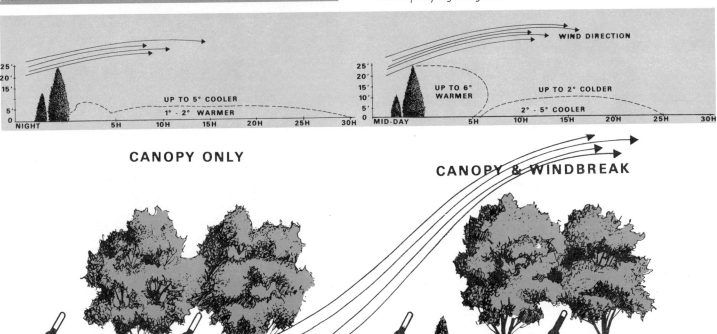

Where there is free air movement, there is little or no difference between actual air temperatures in sun or shade. However, under trees flanked by shrubs reflecting air currents upward, there will be cooler temperatures in the shade.

DEAD-AIR INSULATION An evergreen or row of evergreens placed next to a wall create an area of "dead" air between plants and wall. This acts much the same as the dead airspace in the wall of a house. The temperature gradient between the inside of the building and the dead airspace is reduced and held relatively constant, thus preventing the escape of heat from the building. Without the evergreens, air currents would maintain a high temperature gradient and facilitate the escape of warm air through the wall. Of necessity, such evergreens must be of a dense nature in the manner of *Arborvitae*, hemlock (*Thuja*), or spruce (*Picea*), and must be planted close together to form a solid wall.

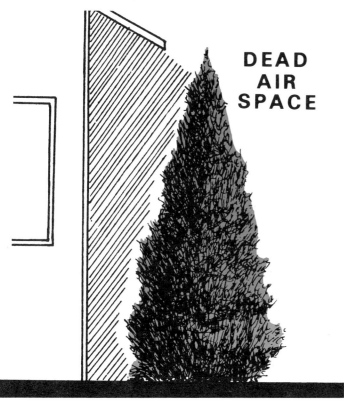

DEAD AIR SPACE

With a 70° F. constant house temperature, the amount of fuel saved by a building protected from the wind is 22.9 percent. Victor and Aladar Olgyay estimate that with good protection on three sides of the building, the fuel savings might run as high as 30 percent.[34]

A by-product of such evergreen placement may be a cooling effect in summer, depending, of course, on orientation and placement. Plants slow the upward flow of warm air directly under them during the early evening hours, thus providing a tent of warmer air on cool summer evenings.

The deciduous tree canopy combined with a coniferous windbreak planting will furnish a pleasant sheltered area under the overstory. Although shaded from the wind during the day, the air retains a certain amount of the day's warmth well into the evening, while still affording wind protection.

COLD-AIR POCKETS When wind disturbance is greatly reduced and air stops moving, thermal stratification and stagnation of the air may occur within a sheltered area, resulting in greater frost danger.

Cool air is heavier than warm air and behaves somewhat like water flowing toward the lowest points. In hilly and other rough lands, a well-marked local temperature effect is often noted in valleys or depressions into which the cold air sinks during the summer nights. This flood of cold air causes "cold islands" or "cold air puddles." Accordingly, any elevation that impedes the flow of air affects the distribution of the nocturnal temperature by creating a damming action; concave terrain formations become cold air lakes at night. The same phenomenon is greater when a large volume of cold airflow is involved, as in valleys. The temperature at the plateau will be cold; at the valley floor very cold; but the higher sides of the slopes will remain warm. On benchlands and the upper slopes of tablelands the temperature may be 6° to 10°F. or more above that of the valley below. Such temperature inversions are particularly marked on cold, calm nights, in arid or semi-arid regions where there is little cover to prevent rapid radiation. Sometimes the line of temperature variations is very marked. It often creates distinct air currents as it pours down mountain canyons by night.

EVERGREEN PLANTS STOP COLD AIR FLOW

DECIDUOUS PLANTS FILTER COLD AIR FLOW

[34]Victor and Aladar Olgyay, *Design with Climate* (Princeton, 1963), p. 34.

HEATED AIR During the day, hot air formed over unshaded ground rises vertically, and thus has little influence upon the temperature of the air under adjacent shade. During the nights, however, cold air formed over open ground spreads out readily to and under the adjacent cover.

These phenomena are what Dr. Aloys Bernatzky, writing in "Anthos" magazine (1966, issue 1), is discussing when he talks about the balancing of temperatures between the green areas of the city and the built-up areas, having a beneficial effect on the climate of the city. In this article he says:

. . . the masses of the building of a city form an artificial rock that stores up heat during the daytime. Not only with the ground surface, but with all the walls of the buildings as well, and they make up a total far greater than the area itself. And as the masses of the buildings reduce the effects of air currents, the process of carrying off this stored up heat is slowed down. In addition to this, the amount of heat which on plant covered areas is absorbed by the process of assimilation and evaporation remains practically intact in the areas of the city where there is no vegetation at all. The values measured were found to be exceptionally high (60,000 K/cal/per year/per m²). During daytime the centers of the cities can have a higher temperature than that of the surrounding countryside, and the average figures for a whole year show over-temperatures of 0.5 to 1.5 centigrade in the cities. This corresponds to lowering the altitude of the city with respect to sea-level by 100 to 300 meters and means a change from normal climate to a more unhealthy climate. At the same time atmospheric humidity is reduced, resulting in an increase of diseases affecting the respiratory organs.[35]

Manmade surfaces, then, exaggerate temperature extremes. Because plant materials absorb radiation and release it more slowly, plants are able to decrease temperature extremes. Highly reflective, manmade surfaces absorb heat to a large extent and release it rapidly, causing an overheated environment. Plant materials, on the other hand, absorb a greater amount of solar radiation during the daytime and release it slowly at night, reducing diurnal temperature variations.

Plant materials, especially in the case of deciduous trees, interfere with solar radiation and reduce radiation reflection, causing a temperature reduction, not only in the shade of the tree, but immediately adjacent to it.

The foliage of deciduous trees intercept solar radiation during the hottest part of the year, and their bare branches do not interfere appreciably with the winter sun, during a time when its warmth is desirable.

[35] Aloys Bernatzky, "Climatic Influences of the Greens and City Planning," *Anthos*, v. 1 (1966), p. 24.

esthetic uses
of plants

ESTHETIC VALUES

Plants are beautiful and stimulating to the senses. Poems have been written about the beauty of flowers, foliage, plants, trees, and shrubs. Writers have proclaimed plants to be full of charm, grace, and endless excitement. In an increasingly manmade world, plants are a welcome relief because of their diversity of form, color, and texture. Their primary use in our environment *is* esthetic. The planting designer is consciously using, exploiting, and emphasizing the design characteristics of plant materials.

This beauty need not be handled in a self-conscious, subjective manner. There are copious catalogs of the ways in which plants can be assessed consciously, and objectively used esthetically. The isolation and organization of the esthetic uses of plants by cataloging or listing their characteristics can be an effective tool in exploiting their inherent beauty.

A discussion of the esthetic use of plants may be summarized as follows: If a beautiful element is understood and its potential comprehended through a study of its design characteristics, there are ways to stage it, to exploit it, to use it, to show it off. As the popular saying goes: "If you've got it, flaunt it!"

The ways in which plants may be used esthetically are myriad. The following vocabulary will only suggest some of the observable and potential esthetic uses.

Visual

POSITIVE ELEMENT The plant is a positive element when it is an object to be seen and to be noticed, and when the plant or its parts are what is important or of interest.

NEGATIVE COMPONENT When the view beyond is what is important, the plant directs or blocks. It exists to enframe or outline a view or to serve as a backdrop. It is not noticed for its own sake.

Two-Dimensional Elements

Obviously, any plant is a three-dimensional element. Even the smallest vine, clinging to a smooth wall, has height, depth, and width. However, the esthetic impact of a three-dimensional object may be line and shape appearing on a two-dimensional plane. It may create illusory space, or its form may be reflected or projected on a wall or surface to create line, pattern, or texture. Interest, excitement, and dynamism may be added to the stark walls of contemporary masonry, concrete, or glass through the use of plants.

The shadow—its reflection or silhouette—may be more important esthetically than a plant itself. Visually, the shadow of the plant on a wall may appear as a moving painting.

Plato in his "allegory of the cave," alluded to the forms of objects reflected on the back wall of a cave, and contrasted these reflections with the reality of the actual object. The three-dimensional plant may be the essence of reality, but the abstraction of its form on a stark wall may hold more interest and potential attraction than the object itself.

The two-dimensional esthetic use of plants may vary from day to night. During daylight hours the pattern of plants reflected in curtain walls, glass windows, or still water may be exploited by the planting designer. The shadow of the plant, cast by the sun as it strikes a vertical wall or horizontal floor, may hold as much promise for manipulation as the mass or form of the plant itself.

Night lighting which projects the abstracted plant-form shadow onto a stark wall may reveal much more interest than would the three-dimensional form of the plant itself in the daylight. Backlighting walls behind picturesque trees or shrubs can reveal the flat silhouette of the plant in a stark and striking manner.

A plant used as a silhouette or for its reflection in placid water has two-dimensional esthetic interest.

Flat surface interest and potential must be recognized and utilized when discussing the esthetic usage of plants. At times, the two-dimensional manipulation may be conscious and intentional. At other times, the two-dimensional handling may be an additional bonus resulting from the use of plants in other ways for other purposes.

Three-Dimensional Object

Esthetically, as a plant is moved away from a two-dimensional surface, it becomes a three-dimensional object—an element to be manipulated, arranged, and utilized in realizing or implementing design concepts much as other elements are used in environmental design, with one notable exception. A plant is a changing, living, growing object. It must be remembered that the esthetic use of the plants as three-dimensional objects is the objective handling of subjective elements of great beauty, having inherent evocative qualities.

SCULPTURAL   As a three-dimensional object, the plant may be viewed as a sculptural element.

TEXTURAL   The three-dimensional plant may be viewed as a textural element. In a world full of textures—smooth, polished, rough, craggy, gnarled, rippled, and rugged—manmade elements tend to have a sameness of texture, due to the techniques of processing and manufacture. Plants have limitless textural variations. It is possible to use the textural quality of plants in conjunction with other plants, with architecture, or with other natural or manmade materials.

Parts of plants also have textures which may be used esthetically. Trunks, branches, twigs, roots, and leaves—both on the plant and on the ground—all provide texture. This may be contrasted with other elements or used to complement surrounding textures.

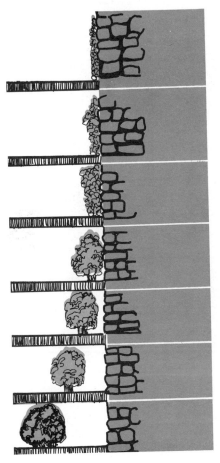

106

NATURALNESS The mere naturalness of a plant may be enough reason to use it esthetically. As more and more man-made elements become stacked one upon the other, there is an ever-increasing need to introduce into the cultural milieu something not created by human endeavor. A plant is the easiest object to use in accomplishing this. Many plants used in congested urban areas are intended primarily for this purpose.

The introduction of a natural element breaks the harshness, the coldness, the starkness of urban architecture. The undisciplined naturalness of a plant and all that this implies is, in a way, symbolic; it may be more of a necessity for the human spirit in an urban age than is commonly realized. The ginkgo tree along the city avenue may be there in deference to the human need to include part of the natural environment in the urban scene.

COLOR The vast palette of color available in plants is a basic esthetic consideration in their use. The various parts of plants have a wide selection of hues, intensities, and values. Trunks, roots, branches, twigs, and leaves all provide color in plants. Plants change color according to the season.

The use of color is tied to dynamic emphasis, accent, decoration, attraction, and organization. Sometimes plants are used merely because they are colorful. Poets, painters, and landscape designers of the past have referred to the use of color in the landscape as painting with plants, or as providing spots or splashes of color in either the natural or manmade landscape.

The esthetic use of plants with regard to color must be considered in relationship to all of their functional uses, and has been adequately covered in planting design books. However, in contemporary urban landscape, the changing colors of plants assume great importance.

Fog Snow Rain

DYNAMIC APPREHENSION

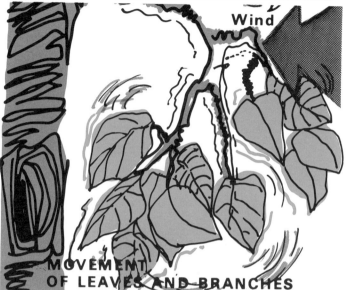

Wind

MOVEMENT OF LEAVES AND BRANCHES

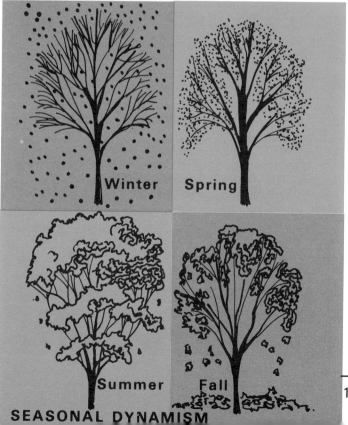

Winter Spring

Summer Fall

SEASONAL DYNAMISM

Life cycle of growth, death, and decay

DYNAMIC Of all the architectural and engineering elements used by the environmental designer, plants are the most dynamic. They are elements which are constantly changing in appearance. Daily, they are lighted sequentially by the sun and the moon, and by artificial night lighting. Seasonally, they undergo the cycle of winter, spring, summer, and autumn. Plants, like man and other animals, go through a cycle of growth, death, and decay.

How plants are perceived is altered by light patterns and moisture. As rain, snow, sleet, or fog alters the human perception of the plant and its form, the plant is viewed as an inherently changeable element.

There are also innate dynamics in the interrelationship of the plant with its environment. The plant is growing and decaying all of its life. The plant is moved by the wind, illuminated by the sun, lacquered by the rain, frosted by the snow, awakened by the spring, denuded by the winter.

A moire pattern is created as wind causes a plant to move to cross and uncross its branches and leaves. The movement of the plant often reveals parts of the view beyond it. The moving shadow pattern of a plant projected on a wall changes as the sun moves and creates a synergism between plant and environment. The plant interacting with the wind gives added movement, life, and character to the scene in which it is placed.

109

VISUAL CONTROLLERS Plants are visually controlling elements. They can be negative elements largely unseen, but accentuating and framing the views beyond.

Masking, relative to screening, controls or heightens esthetic pleasure. To block ugliness, plants are used as masking agents. In doing so, the environmental designer selectively reveals that part of the view which he wishes to be seen, and conceals that which he does not wish to be seen.

View direction is saying with plants: "This is what I want you to see completely! This is what I want you to see partially! This is what I don't want you to see at all!" By using plants to push or pull the view, it is possible to visually control the landscape.

110

Perspective control is stating with plants: "That is far away; I want it to appear even farther away! That is far away; I want to bring it closer! This is close; I want to make it appear closer! Or, this is close; I want it to appear far away!" The environmental designer can make elements appear different, perspectively. He is able to push or pull a view. This may be done by color, size, texture, and degree of interest.

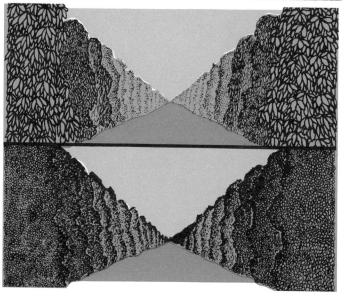

Perceptual control is using elements to heighten esthetic pleasure. It is possible to change the viewer's perception by controlling what he sees, hears, and feels. The designer may consciously provide pleasant views, offer pleasure-giving surfaces to touch, or through the arrangement of plants take advantage of the effects of air. This conscious use of plants may give the viewer both conscious and subconscious pleasure.

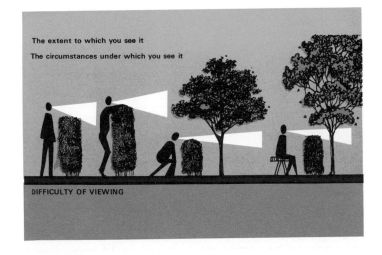

The extent to which you see it

The circumstances under which you see it

DIFFICULTY OF VIEWING

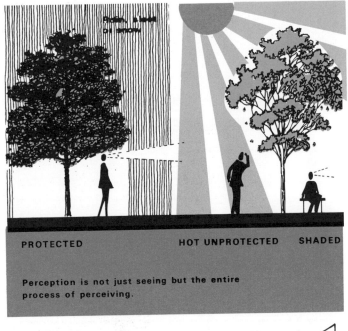

PROTECTED   HOT UNPROTECTED   SHADED

Perception is not just seeing but the entire process of perceiving.

Complementors

There are two aspects to the use of plants esthetically as complementary elements. The first of these is to complete or finish the setting. This may be a space, a building form, a view or a physical or conceptual idea, which is left to be completed at the planting stage of a design project.

The second aspect of the complementary usage of plants is to complement something which already exists, either manmade or natural. This may be done by using plant form, color or texture.

Attractors

Plants are used esthetically because they attract things to themselves. Birds may be attracted to plants because of their berries, nuts, fruits, or for their potential shelter. Animals may be attracted because they offer food or shelter or safety.

People are attracted by plants because of their color, odor, shade, beauty, texture, or because of their food and shelter value. The recognition of plants as being attractive is essential to understanding their esthetic use. Plants may be used esthetically, not only because of their inherent attractiveness, but also because they attract people, birds, and other animals.

Unifiers

Plants are unifiers, synthesizers, and organizers; they are used to give visual coherence to a scene, to pull together disparate elements, and to organize divergent parts of a scene or facility. They can be used to give a feeling of uniformity and harmony in a world of diverse, unorganized, and visually chaotic components.

Signs of all shapes and sizes, wires, buildings of all ages and kinds, and automobiles, all contribute to the visual chaos of the environment. The manmade environment is characterized by lack of unity in spite of conformity, and visual disorganization in spite of apparent relationship. Plants have a calming, unifying, and organizing quality. Because of their relative similarity, color, form, and texture, they are the unifiers, synthesizers, and organizers. Street trees, for example form the linkage or the vital arteries between parks and other green areas in the city.

Emphasizers

Plants can be used as emphasizers, accentuators, and punctuators. The designer can use them to say: "This is it! This is the most important thing in the landscape!"

Plants used as exclamation points give emphasis to locations or elements in the environment. When something is happening, plants can be used to call attention to a change of direction, known as a "knuckle."

Vast open farm fields of the Middle West are punctuated by windbreaks of trees, farmsteads, and cemeteries.

Points in the "goose-foot" city pattern of Washington, D.C., are accentuated by green triangular parks and plantings in traffic circles.

Entrance to a shopping center

Emphasizing the entrance to a building

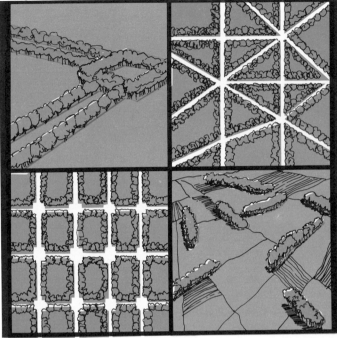

Diverters

Plants may be used for diverting attention, for hiding, or for attracting attention in another direction. The designer is saying: "This beautiful thing is more inviting than that ugliness." Plants used in this manner are effective on highways, where movement is fast and perception quick. Even viewed from a bicycle, the esthetic use of plants for diversion is more effective than when observed at a walking pace.

Two ways of utilizing the esthetic qualities of plants to divert the eye of the viewer are to provide screening to block an ugly view, and provide something more attractive, diverting attention from the ugly view.

Softeners

We live in a hard, jagged world full of sharp edges and noisy parts. Visual lubrication or green liquidity is needed to assuage and mollify the oppressive harshness of man's surroundings. The rounded forms of plants soften and smooth the severity of individual buildings, and abate the over-all crescendo of the manmade environment.

Acknowledgers

Plants can be used to acknowledge that something exists and to indicate its location. They call attention to items or elements which are most important; when added at the end of the design continuum, they provide recognition.

To acknowledge or to indicate is to point out existence. Plants may indicate the location or importance of an object or even point out divergent land uses.

ACKNOWLEDGEMENT

Decorators

The greatest misuse of plant materials occurs in their use as "decorations." This happens when plants are used as street furniture, "googlies," doo-dads, adornments, ornaments, embellishments, enrichments, garnishments, and "beautification." Topiary and espalier plants fall within the esthetic use of plants as decorative elements.

115

Plants have always been used this way. In manipulating plants in these grotesque ways, man shows his "superiority" over nature in his ability to make them conform to his whims. Such plants are "cute," are "conversation pieces." This legitimate, though perverted, use of plants provides the miniaturization and capsulization of nature, in the increasingly urbanized world. Man says in this way, "I have not only captured nature, but I have controlled it and manipulated it."

Articulators

Articulation of elements in a design, using plants for circulation, entrances, service areas, private areas, and public areas, can make such areas clearer and more distinct. Plants can be used to articulate the elements of a design; they can be used for clarification, delineation, and emphasis. Instead of just adding plants to a completed design, it is possible to use plants to define the existing elements. Plants can and should be used to substantiate other design statements. Their form, color, texture, size, and scale can be used to assist in the articulation of the design elements.

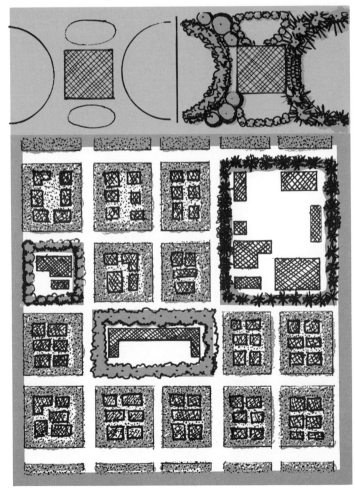

Articulation of hierarchies is the use of plants to recognize the relative importance of each of the elements in design. Generally, there are first, second, and third areas of priority in landscape design. These are established by the designer and include parking areas, service areas, and entrance areas. Some are more important than others. This hierarchy must be acknowledged and articulated by the use of plants. According to the designer's concept the texture, color, form, richness, interest, and spatial volume of plants can be used as a build-up to create a progression or a regression in the mind of the user.

The hierarchal system is expressed in any physical design. Plants should substantiate and reinforce the designer's hierarchal concept, rather than being merely addenda and beautification elements. This is design reinforcement and accentuation through the use of plants as positive design elements in hierarchal articulation.

Articulation of concepts is using plants to supplement and give form to a concept. Plants are used to complete the designer's statement of: "Here is what I had in mind—a room, a corridor!"

Physical design is the concept formulated. It is giving body to an idea. Plants are used functionally to clothe the concept. Used in conjunction with circulation, they emphasize speed, repose, or rest.. They indicate direction of movement, view, and degree of importance.

Design gives physical form to a thought or a concept. Plants are design elements which functionally assist in doing this. The scale, texture, and form of plants all assist the designer in realizing his ideas. Concepts may be articulated on a small or a large scale.

Articulation may be used to reinforce design structure in the city, to link urban open spaces, and to reinforce the overall city pattern. For example, a street-tree planting hierarchy can indicate residential, commercial, and industrial areas of a city.

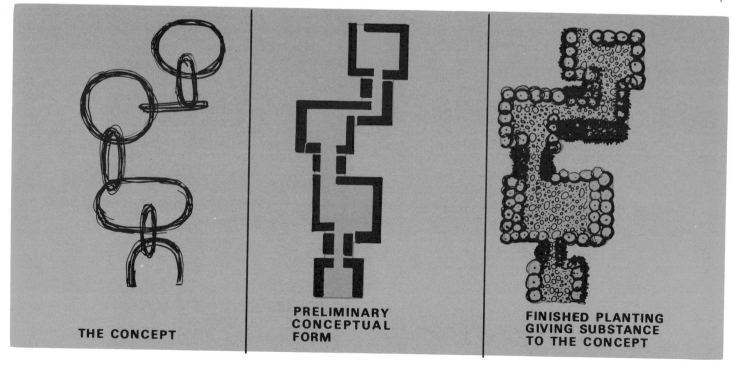

THE CONCEPT

PRELIMINARY CONCEPTUAL FORM

FINISHED PLANTING GIVING SUBSTANCE TO THE CONCEPT

Indicators

Area indicators are plants used to delineate the presence or distinctiveness of an area.

The significance or importance of an area can be defined or reinforced by the selection and placement of plants.

Encircling an area, under a canopy, behind a windbreak, in a sun pocket are ways to indicate areas. Plants can be used both to create a special place and to indicate that it *is* special.

With plants, the designer says: "This is it over here, or that's it over there."

Event indicators are plants used as memorials.

A grove of trees, a single specimen, a woods or mass planting—all may be used to indicate that an event has occurred at a specific location. With them the designer is saying: "At this place . . . this tree commemorates . . . ."

Personality indicators are plants used as a memorial to individuals They say: "This tree planted in memory of . . . . These trees were donated by . . . . This tree is a memorial to . . . ."

Object indicators are plants used as an object or as sculpture. They indicate the beauty of natural elements.

Scale indicators are plants used to maintain human scale in the midst of gargantuan architecture. Trees are familiar objects and have a fairly uniform size and scale to which humans can relate. In the super-human scale of the city or of a vast natural landscape, trees and other plants indicate the relative size of surroundings by introducing the element of known scale. This is the use of plants only to indicate scale, not to alter it, modulate it, or change the perception of it.

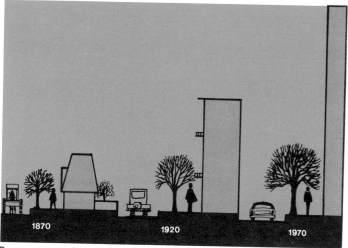

1870 1920 1970

Parameter indicators are plants used to define the limits of a site, of a property, or of an area. Plants can be used to indicate property lines or the parts of a larger landscape. With them the designer says: "These are the outer limits!"

Fence rows, property hedges, peripheral planting, and hedgerows indicate the outer limits or the parameters of specific areas.

Place indicators are plants used to create a sense of place. When used in this way, the viewer associates with it: "Under the willows." "Beside the oak." "In the shade of the old apple tree."

Because of the character of the planting, parks, plazas, and miniparks have a sense of place. In any surrounding, it is helpful to create a sense of place to which a user can relate.

Modulators

Scale modulation is the altering of the apparent or perceived scale through the introduction of plants. The texture, size, form, and color of plants can be used by the designer to vary the apparent scale, thus convincing the viewer he is seeing something different than what actually exists.

Plants can be used to reduce and enlarge the apparent scale. Small-scale plants can cause the observer to feel taller than he actually is. Extremely large-scale trees can cause the observer to feel smaller than he is. In the city among tall buildings, mature trees reduce the apparent size of the architecture, because of their modulation of scale.

OVERSIZE TREES   UNDERSIZE TREES   BONSAI TREES

MODULATION OF THE PERCEPTION OF SCALE

Perspective modulation occurs when the color, texture, size, and form of plants are used to modulate perceived perspective. Plants can push a view into the distance, or pull it close to the observer.

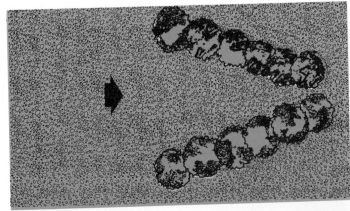

Light modulation is the use of plants to change light patterns. The beautiful and varied shadow patterns cast by plants can be manipulated and used esthetically by the imaginative planting designer. Light modulation is using plants with natural or artificial light for esthetic purposes. It is the use of shadows, back-lighting, silhouetting, and highlighting. Shadows may be cast on walls or floors, or on natural or manmade elements, such as rock walks, walls, fences, and architecture.

Symbol-Surrogate

This term refers to the symbolic use of individual plants as substitutes for the natural environment. This is the miniaturization of the landscape, the reduction of scale to maintain the essence of nature in a microcosm. This is our heritage—plants growing symbolically in yard-square holes in the sidewalk.

Evocators

Plants may be used esthetically to evoke memories of other times, of other places, of feelings, of an attitude, of a way of thinking. They may be used to summon or bring forth innate feelings for the natural environment.

Under a shade tree in a city park, one can imagine that he is far from civilization, in a wild and natural landscape.

Intangibles Made Tangible

This is best defined by examples. Shade makes one aware of sun. Hearing the sound of the wind in pines or the rustle of oak leaves, makes one more aware of the leaves on trees, and the wind. A plant can make one aware of his age. "Look how this tree has grown since I planted it!" City dwellers, who are generally aware of changing seasons via clothing displays in store windows, may also experience seasonal change because of the changing coloration of the plants.

Mood Delineators

Plants affect people's moods because of their sense of shelter, permanence, privacy, or apartness. They create feelings of sadness, pensiveness, happiness, or exuberance. For example, the mood of the springtime landscape of southern France has been captured forever on canvas by Van Gogh in his painting of the ever-moving cypresses; similarly the mood of springtime in a mid-Atlantic American city is not only indelibly recorded in the human mind, but presented anew each year in all its fresh reality by the masses of pink magnolia blooms in an urban park.

Sound

Leaves on the trees or on the ground can rustle and create pleasing sounds. Plants attract animals which create sounds. The wind moving through plants creates sensually stimulating sounds to the hearer.

Odor

The flowers and foliage of plants create pleasant scents. The blossoms of magnolia and honeysuckle, the leaves of eucalyptus are examples of fragrant parts of plants which exude pleasant scents.

Touch

The tactile quality of twigs, branches, trunks, and leaves of plants call attention to their esthetic qualities. They invite people to touch them.

As culture becomes more urbanized, the environmental designers will acknowledge, chronicle, and utilize the esthetic value of plants for their functions.

125

conclusion

This book is a beginning. It outlines an elementary vocabulary and a way of thinking and communicating facts about plants. This publication has been a review of what is known and what has been done in regard to the functional abilities of plants to alter or ameliorate the environment. Hopefully, more existing research will be brought to light. In any case, much more needs to be known; more research into plant materials needs to be conducted and made available to the environmental designer. It is hoped that a refined and expanded vocabulary will be developed beyond that which has been expressed in this book. Hopefully, a re-orientation of thinking about plants as environmental design elements will also be realized and this work will provide a stimulus for further activity.

This book expresses the fact that plants are multi-faceted. They provide recreation and relief, but they also provide environmental control and amelioration.

Most plants serve many purposes. Few functional problems exist in isolation; therefore, each plant is multi-functional. The functional uses of plant materials are intricately and inextricably intertwined and interconnected. The isolation and single dimensionality exhibited in this organizational system is artificial and seldom exists in the usage of plants in reality. A rational, objective methodology will become increasingly necessary in utilizing plant materials to solve environmental problems.

bibliography

PREFACE

Johnson, Philip. "Why We Want Our Cities Ugly," in Smithsonian Institution, *The Fitness of Man's Environment*. Washington, D.C., Smithsonian Institution Press, 1968.

PLANTS AND CONTEMPORARY LIFE

Kaplan, Abraham. *31 Minds Explore Our Environment*. Report of the Committee on Environmental Design, National Association of Home Builders, 1965.

Peter, Lawrence J., and Raymond Hull. *The Peter Principle*. New York, William Morrow & Co., 1969.

White, Morton and Lucia. *The Intellectual Versus the City*. New York, Mentor Books, 1964.

FUNCTIONAL USE OF PLANTS

Hall, Edward T. *The Silent Language*. Greenwich, Conn., Fawcett, 1965.

Kinne, Russ, in a book review of *Trees* by Andreas Feininger. *Popular Photography*, June 1969.

ARCHITECTURAL USE OF PLANTS

Cullen, Gordon. *Townscape*. New York, Reinhold, 1961.

Dewolfe, Ivor. *Italian Townscape*. London, Architectural Press, 1964.

Eckbo, Garrett. *The Art of Home Landscaping*. New York, F. W. Dodge, 1965.

———. *Landscape for Living*. New York, F. W. Dodge, 1961.

Goldfinger, Erno. "The Sensation of Space," *Architectural Review*, November 1941, December 1941, January 1942.

Leonard, Michael. "Humanizing Space," *Progressive Architecture*, April 1969.

Lynch, Kevin. *Site Planning*. Cambridge, Massachusetts Institute of Technology Press, 1962.

Martel, Donald J. "Architectural Aspects of Plants," *Arborist's News*, v. 27, June 1962.

Rose, James. *Creative Gardens*. New York, Reinhold, 1958.

Simonds, John Ormsbee. *Landscape Architecture: The Shaping of Man's Natural Environment*. New York, F. W. Dodge, 1961.

Spreirigen, Paul. *Urban Design: The Architecture of Towns and Cities*. New York, McGraw-Hill, 1965.

Privacy Control

Chermayeff, Serge, and Christopher Alexander. *Community and Privacy*. Garden City, Doubleday, 1963.

Simonds, John Ormsbee. *Landscape Architecture: The Shaping of Man's Natural Environment*. New York, F. W. Dodge, 1961.

ENGINEERING USE OF PLANTS

Acoustical Control

American Association of State Highway Officials, Committee Proceedings, December 1964.

———. "Highway Noise Reduced Through Border Planting," *American Highways*, v. 32, July 1953.

———. *Landscape Design Guide*. Washington, D.C., 1965.

Aylor, Donald. *Can Plants Filter Noise from Our Environment?* Unpublished manuscript. New Haven, Connecticut Agricultural Experiment Station, 1970.

Bach, Wilfrid, and Edward Mathews. *The Importance of Green Areas in Urban Planning*. Paper prepared for the workshop "Bioclimatology and Environmental Health," Public Health Service, U.S. Department of Health, Education, and Welfare, Cincinnati, Ohio, July 14–16, 1969.

Baron, Robert Alex. "The Invisible Polluter—Noise," *Catalyst for Environmental Quality*, Spring 1970.

Beranek, Leo L. *Acoustics*. New York, McGraw-Hill, 1954.

———. *Noise Reduction*. New York, McGraw-Hill, 1960.

Bruel, J. F., and K. C. Kjaer. *Acoustic Noise Measurements* (Manual). Denmark, 1969.

Conservation Foundation. *Newsletter*. Washington, D.C., December 29, 1967.

Cook, David I., and David F. van Haverbeke. *Trees and Shrubs for Noise Abatement*. Paper presented at the symposium on "Trees and Forests in an Urbanizing Environment." Amherst, University of Massachusetts, 1970.

Embleton, T. F. W. Personal correspondence with M. R. Guthrie of Louisville, Ky., July 30, 1970. (Embleton was then with the Acoustical Section, Division of Physics, National Research Council of Canada, Ottawa.)

————. "Sound Propagation in Homogenous, Deciduous and Evergreen Woods," *Journal of the Acoustical Society of America*, v. 33, August 1963.

Eyring, Carl F. "Jungle Acoustics," *Journal of the Acoustical Society of America*, v. 18, October 1946.

Highway Research Board. *Selected Bibliography on Vehicle Noise and Fumes*. Highway Research Board Bibliography 22, Publication 614. Washington, D.C., Highway Research Board. 1958.

————. *Can Noise Radiation from Highways Be Reduced by Design?* Highway Research Record 232. Washington, D.C., Highway Research Board, 1968.

————. *Effect of Landscape Development on Nearby Property*. National Cooperative Highway Research Report 75. Washington, D.C., Highway Research Board, 1969.

————. *Highway Noise: Measurement, Simulation and Mixed Reactions*. National Cooperative Highway Research Report 78. Washington, D.C., Highway Research Board, 1969.

————. *Roadside Planting to Reduce Traffic Noise*. Report of the Committee on Roadside Development. Washington, D.C., Highway Research Board, 1956.

Hoover, Robert M. Personal correspondence with the author, August 8, 1967. (Hoover is with the acoustical consulting firm of Bolt, Beranek and Newman of Cambridge, Mass.)

Knudsen, Vern O. Personal correspondence with the author, August 9, 1967. (At that time, Knudsen was Professor of Physics, Emeritus, University of California, Los Angeles.)

Knudsen, Vern O., and Cyril M. Harris. *Acoustical Designing in Architecture*. New York, Wiley, 1950.

Kryopoulos, Peter. "Traffic Noise," *Traffic Quarterly*, January 1948.

Margules, Stanley Raymond. *Propagation of Noise in the Landscape Environment*. Unpublished M.S. thesis. Davis, University of California, 1956. (Summary by Richard Harris.)

Meister, F. J. "Die Dammung von Verkehrsgerauschen durch Grünanlagen" (The Reduction of Traffic Noise by Vegetation). Dusseldorf, v. 101. (Verlag Deutsches Institut—Zeitschrift Bord, 1959.)

————. "Uber einige Besonderheiten der Schallausbreitung auf natürlich bewachsenen Flächen" (Some Properties of Noise Distribution Across Natural Vegetation), 3d International Congress on Acoustics, *Proceedings*, Stuttgart, 1959.

Moore, John E. *Design for Noise Reduction*. London, Architectural Press, 1966.

Reethof, Gerard. *Noise Information and Data*. Unpublished manuscript. Blooming Grove Hunting and Fishing Club, State College, 1970.

Rettinger, M. "Noise Abatement by Barriers," *Progressive Architecture*, August 1965.

————. "Noise Level Reduction of Barriers," *Noise Control*, v. 3, September 1952.

Rudnick, I. "Propagation of Sound in the Open Air," in C. M. Harris, ed., *Handbook of Noise Control*. New York, McGraw-Hill, 1957.

Seikman, William. Personal correspondence with the author, May 9, 1969. (Seikman is the Director of the Illinois Institute of Technology Research Institute, Riverbank Acoustical Laboratory, Geneva, Ill.)

————. "Outdoor Acoustical Treatment, Grass and Trees," *Journal of the Acoustical Society of America*, v. 46, pt. 1, April 1969.

Sexton, Burton. "Traffic Noise," *Traffic Quarterly*, July 1969.

Simonson, Wilbur H. "Abatement of Highway Noise with Special Reference to Roadside Design." Highway Research Bulletin No. 110, publication 363, Abatement of Highway Noise and Fumes," Washington, D.C. Highway Research Board, National Research Council, 1957.

Stephenson, J. R., and G. H. Vulkan. "Traffic Noise," *Journal of Sound and Vibration*, v. 2, no. 7, 1969.

Stevens, K. N., and R. H. Bolt. "On the Shielding of Noise Outdoors," *Journal of the Acoustical Society of America* (abstract), v. 26, 1954.

Thiessen, G. J. *Community Noise—Surface Transportation*.

Paper presented at a meeting of the Acoustical Society of America, November 13, 1969.

Weiner, Francis M., and David N. Keast. "Sound Propagation Over Terrain," *Journal of the Acoustical Society of America*, v. 31, June 1959.

Atmospheric Purification

Bach, Wilfrid, and Edward Mathews. *The Importance of Green Areas in Urban Planning*. Paper prepared for the workshop "Bioclimatology and Environmental Health," Public Health Service, U.S. Department of Health, Education, and Welfare, Cincinnati, Ohio, July 14–16, 1969.

Bernatzsky, Aloys. "Climatic Influences of the Greens and City Planning," *Anthos*, no. 1, 1966.

————. "The Performance and Value of Trees," *Anthos*, no. 1, 1969.

Cole, Lamont C. "Are We Running Out of Oxygen?" *Catalyst for Environmental Quality*, Spring 1970.

Geiger, Rudolph. *The Climate Near the Ground*. Cambridge, Harvard University Press, 1950.

McCurdy, Thomas R. *Vehicular Emissions and the Location of Highways in Urban Areas*. Thesis. Center for Air Environment Studies, State College, Pennsylvania State University, 1969.

Waggoner, Paul E., as quoted by Tom Stevenson, "How Green Plants Help Fight Against Air Pollution," *Washington Post*, August 2, 1970. (Waggoner is the Chief Climatologist at the Connecticut Agricultural Experiment Station, New Haven.)

Traffic Control

White, Andrew J. *Study of Marginal and Median Tree and Shrub Planting as Safety Barriers on Highways*. South Lee, N. H., Motor Vehicle Research, Inc., 1953.

CLIMATOLOGICAL USES OF PLANTS

American Society of Heating and Ventilating Engineers. *Carrier Psychometric Chart*. New York, 1946.

Architect's Journal. *Building Environment Handbooks*. London, October 1968–January 1969.

Aronin, Jeffrey E. *Climate and Architecture*. New York, Reinhold, 1953.

Brooks, Charles Ernest P. *Climate in Everyday Life*. London, Ernest Benn, 1950.

————. *Selective Annotated Bibliography on Urban Climates*. Meteorological Abstracts and Bibliography, v. 3. Boston, American Meteorological Society, 1952.

Brooks, F. A. *An Introduction to Physical Microclimatology*. Davis, University of California, 1959.

Brunt, D. "Some Factors in Microbioclimatology," *The Quarterly Journal of the Royal Meteorological Society*, v. 71, no. —, 1945.

Claiborne, Robert. *Climate, Man and History*. New York, W. W. Norton & Co., 1970.

De La Rue, E. Aubert. *Man and the Winds*. New York, Philosophical Library, 1955.

Egli, Ernest. *Climate and Town Districts; Consequences and Demands*. Zurich, Verlag Für Architectur-Erlenbach, 1951.

Emerick, R. H. "Comfort Factors Affecting Cooling Design," *Progressive Architecture*, December 1951.

Fitch, James M. *American Building: The Forces That Shape It*. Boston, Houghton-Mifflin, 1948.

Geiger, Rudolph. *The Climate Near the Ground*. Cambridge, Harvard University Press, 1950.

————. "Microclimatology," in American Meteorological Society, *Compendium of Meteorology*. American Meteorological Society, 1951.

Herrington, L. P. *Human Factors in Planning for Climate Control*. Building Research Advisory Board Conference Report No. 1. Washington, D.C., Building Research Advisory Board, 1952.

House Beautiful, "The Climate Controlled House," a series of monthly articles, October 1949 through January 1951.

Huntington, Ellsworth. *The Human Habitat*. Princeton, D. Van Nostrand Co., 1927.

————. *Principles of Human Geography*. 6th ed. New York, John Wiley and Sons, 1951.

Kittredge, J. *Forest Influences*. New York, McGraw-Hill, 1948.

Klima-Wetter-Mensch Symposium, Leipzig, Quelle und Meyer, 1938.

Koppen, W., and Geiger, R. *Handbuch der Klimatologie.* Berlin, Gebrüder Borntraeger, 1936.

Kratzer, P. Albert. *The Climate of Cities.* Translated by the U.S. Air Force City and Regional Laboratory, Central Forces Scientific and Technical Institute, Braunscheweig, Vieweg und Sohn, 1962.

Landsberg, Helmut. *Physical Climatology.* State College, Pennsylvania State University, 1942.

Landsberg, H. W. "The Climate of Towns," in W. L. Thomas, ed., *Man's Role in Changing the Face of the Earth.* Chicago, University of Chicago Press, 1956.

Lowry, William P. "The Climate of Cities," *Scientific American,* v. 217, no. 2, 1967.

———. *Weather and Life: An Introduction to Biometeorology.* New York, Academic Press, 1969.

Markham, S. F. *Climate and the Energy of Nations.* London, Oxford University Press, 1947.

Munn, R. E. *Descriptive Micrometeorology.* New York, Academic Press, 1966.

Myrup, Leonard O. "A Numerical Model of the Urban Heat Island," *Journal of Applied Meteorology,* v. 8, no. 3, 1969.

"Nature's Own Cooling System," *Nursery Business,* September–October 1970.

Nyberg, A. "Temperature Measurements in An Air Layer Very Close to A Snow Surface," *Geographiska Annaler,* v. 20, no. 8, 1938.

Olgyay, Victor. *Bioclimatic Approach to Architecture.* Building Research Advisory Board Conference Report No. 5. Washington, D.C., National Research Council, 1953.

———. "The Temperate House," *Architectural Forum,* v. 94, March 1959.

Olgyay, Victor and Aladar. "Environment and Building Shape," *Architectural Forum,* v. 101, August 1954.

———. *Solar Control and Shading Devices.* Princeton, Princeton University Press, 1957.

———. "The Theory of Sol-Air Orientation," *Architectural Forum,* v. 100, March 1954.

Olgyay, Victor and Aladar, and Associates. *Application of Climatic Data to House Design.* Washington, D.C., U.S. Housing and Home Finance Agency, 1953.

Peterson, James T. *The Climate of Cities: A Survey of Recent Literature.* Washington, D.C., U.S. Department of Health, Education, and Welfare, 1969.

Ramdas, L. A., R. J. Kalamkar, and K. M. Gadre. "Architectural Studies in Microclimatology," *Indian Journal of Agricultural Science,* v. 4, no. 12, 1934 and v. 5, no. 1, 1935.

"Regional Climate Analysis and Design Data," *Bulletin of the American Institute of Architects,* November 1949–January 1952.

Ruch, T. C. "Somatic Sensations," in T. C. Ruch and H. D. Patton, eds., *Physiology and Biophysics.* 19th ed. Philadelphia, Saunders, 1965.

Scaetta, M. H. "Terminologique, Bioclimatique, et Microclimatique," *Meteorologique,* v. 31, July 1935.

Specht, R. L. *Micro-environment [Soil] of a Natural Plant Community.* Proceedings Canberra Symposium. Paris, United Nations Educational, Social, and Cultural Organization, 1956.

Sutton, O. G. *Micrometeorology.* New York, McGraw-Hill, 1953.

Tait, G. W. C. "The Vertical Temperature Gradient in the Lower Atmosphere Under Daylight Conditions," *The Quarterly Journal of the Royal Meteorological Society,* v. 75, no. 7, 1949.

Trewartha, Glenn T. *An Introduction to Weather and Climate.* New York, McGraw-Hill, 1943.

U.S. Department of Agriculture. *Climate and Man.* Washington, D.C., U.S. Government Printing Office, 1941.

Vernon, H. M., and T. Bedford. "Environmental Warmth and Human Comfort," *British Journal of Applied Physics,* v. 73, February 1950.

Solar Radiation Control

American Society of Heating, Refrigerating and Air Conditioning Engineers. *Shade Factors.* New York, 1960.

Angstrom, A. "The Albedo of Various Surfaces of Ground," *Geographiska Annaler,* v. 7, no. 3, 1927.

Aronin, Jeffrey E. *Climate and Architecture.* New York, Reinhold, 1953.

Bardet, Gaston. "Le Factor Soliel en Urbanisme," *Techniques et Architecture,* v. 18, July 1945.

Becker, C. F. "Solar Radiation Availability on Surfaces in the U.S. As Affected by Season, Orientation, Latitude, Altitude and

Cloudiness," *Journal of Solar Energy Science and Engineering*, v. 8, no. 4, 1957.

Fritz, S. "The Albedo of Ground and Atmosphere," *Bulletin of the American Meteorological Society*, v. 29, no. 6, 1948.

Gates, D. M., and W. Tantraporn. "The Reflectivity of Deciduous Trees and Herbaceous Plants in the Infrared to 25 Microns," *Science*, v. 94, no. 11, 1948.

Geiger, Rudolph. *The Climate Near the Ground*. Cambridge, Mass., Harvard University Press, 1950.

Hand, Irving F. "Charts to Obtain Solar Altitudes and Azimuths," *Heating and Ventilating*, v. 38, October 1948.

Neubauer, L. W. *The Solaranger*. Davis, University of California, 1949.

Olgyay, Aladar. *Shading and Insolation Measurement of Models*. Austin, University of Texas Press, 1953.

Olgyay, Victor and Aladar. *Design With Climate*. Princeton, Princeton University Press, 1963.

Penndorf, R. "Luminous Reflectance (Visual Albedo) of National Objects," *Bulletin of the American Meteorological Society*, v. 37, no. 5, 1956.

Ramadas, L. A., and S. L. Malurkar. "Surface Convection and Variation of Temperature Near a Hot Surface," *Indian Journal of Physics*, v. 7, no. 7, 1927.

Sato, S. "Calculations of the Received Solar Radiation in the Shade of Windbreak at Miyazaki City," *Journal of Agricultural Meteorology* (Tokyo), v. 11, no. 6, 1955.

Solarometer. Toledo, Libby-Owens-Ford Glass Co., 1948.

Sun Angle Calculator. Toledo, Libby-Owens-Ford Glass Co., 1950.

Van der Linde, R. J., and J. P. M. Woudenberg. "A Method for Determining the Daily Variations in Width of a Shadow in Connection with the Time of the Year and the Orientation of the Overshadowing Object," *Journal of the Netherlands Meteorological Institute*, v. 102, no. 2, 1946.

Wright, Henry N. *Solar Radiation as Related to Summer Cooling and Winter Heating in Residences*. John B. Pierce Foundation Report. New York, John B. Pierce Foundation, 1936.

Wind Control

Bach, Wilfrid, and Edward Mathews. *The Importance of Green Areas in Urban Planning*. Paper prepared for the workshop "Bioclimatology and Environmental Health," Public Health Service, U.S. Department of Health, Education, and Welfare, Cincinnati, Ohio, July 14-16, 1969.

Bates, Carlos G. *The Windbreak as a Farm Asset*, Farmers Bulletin 1405 revised. Washington, D.C., U.S. Department of Agriculture, 1944.

————. *Windbreaks: Their Influence and Value*. U.S. Forest Service Bulletin 86. Washington, D.C., Government Printing Office, 1911.

Beddall, J. L. *Hedges for Farm and Garden*. London, Faber and Faber, 1950.

Blenk, H. "Das windschutz Problem um schandienst Grundlagen der Landtechiche, v. 8, no. 1-2, 1953.

Caborn, J. M. *Shelterbelts and Microclimate*. Forestry Commission Bulletin 29. Edinburgh, 1957.

————. *Shelterbelts and Windbreaks*. London, Faber and Faber, 1965.

————. "Width and Cross-sectional Profile in Shelterbelts," International Union of Forest Research Organizations Congress *Proceedings*, v. 12, no. 74, 1963.

Cadman, W. A. *Shelterbelts for Western Hill Farms*. Forest Commission Record 22. London, Her Majesty's Stationery Office, 1963.

Caudill, W. W., and B. H. Reed. *Geometry of Classroom as Related to Natural Lighting and Natural Ventilation*. Texas Engineering Experiment Station Research Report 36. College Station, Texas Engineering Experiment Station, 1952.

Caudill, W. W., S. E. Crites and E. G. Smith. *Some General Considerations in Natural Ventilation of Buildings*. Texas Engineering Experiment Station Report 22. College Station, Texas Engineering Experiment Station, 1951.

Deering, Robert B. "Technology of the Cooling Effect of Trees and Shrubs," *in* Building Research Advisory Board, *Housing and Building in Hot-Humid and Hot-Dry Climates*. Research Conference Report 5. Washington, D.C., Building Research Advisory Council, 1953.

Enrodi, Gabriella. "Effects of the Relief on the March of Temperature in the Tibany Peninsula, Budapest," *Idojarasi*, Orszagos Meteorologiai Intezet, v. 65, no. 10, 1961.

Franken, Ernst. "Uber eine Abhängigkeit der Temperaturverteilung in Strahlungsnachten von Geländeformung u. Windrichtung." (Dependence of Temperature Distribution upon

Topography and Wind Direction.) *Meteorologische Rundschau,* v. 12, January 1959.

Geiger, Rudolph. *The Climate Near the Ground.* Cambridge, Mass., Harvard University Press, 1950.

———. "Mikroklima U. Pflanzenklima," in Koppen, W., and R. Geiger, *Handbuch der Klimatologie.* Berlin, Gebrüder Bornträeger, 1936.

Gorshenin, N. M., and others. *Improvement of Farmland in the Irrigated Region of the Zavoljie.* Union of Soviet Socialist Republic's All-Union Institute of Forest Culture and Forest Melioration Excerpts No. 4., Moscow, Goslestechnisdat, 1934. (U.S. Forest Service Translation No. 64).

Halstead, M. H. "The Relationship Between Wind Structure and Turbulence Near the Ground," *Publications in Climatology,* v. 4, no 3, 1951.

Heywood, G. S. P. "Wind Structure Near the Ground and Its Relation to Temperature Gradient," *The Quarterly Journal of the Royal Meteorological Society,* v. 57, no. 4, 1931.

Hollerman, T. R. *Air Flow Through Conventional Window Openings.* Texas Engineering Experiment Station Research Report 45. College Station, Texas Engineering Experiment Station, 1954.

Houghton, F. C., and C. P. Yaglou. "Cooling Effect on Human Beings Produced by Various Air Velocities," American Society of Heating and Ventilation Engineers, *Transactions,* v. 30, no. 4, 1924.

———. "Determination of the Comfort Zone," American Society of Heating and Ventilation Engineers, *Transactions,* v. 29, no. 673, 1923.

Iizuka, H. *On the Width of Shelterbelts.* Forestry Experiment Station Bulletin 56. Meguro, Japan, 1952.

———. *Wind Erosion Prevention by Windbreaks.* Forestry Experiment Station Bulletin 45. Meguro, Japan, 1950, as cited in *Forestry Abstracts* 286, v. 15, 1954.

Jensen, M., *Shelter Effect.* Copenhagen, The Danish Technical Press, 1954.

Kramer, M. P., A. Assur and M. Rigby. "Selective Annotated Bibliography on Turbulent Diffusion and Micrometeorological Turbulence," in American Meteorological Society, *Meteorological Abstracts and Bibliography,* v. 4. Boston, American Meteorological Society, 1953.

Kreutz, W. *Der Windschutz.* Dortmund, Ardey Verlag, 1952.

———. "Volumänderung der Badenoberfläche in Abhängigkeit vom Wetter," *Meteorologische Rundschau,* v. 6, no. 7, 1950.

Kuehn, E. "Planning the City's Climate," *Landscape,* v. 8, no. 3, 1959.

Kuhlewind, H. F., A. C. Bringmann and D. C. Kaiser. *Richtlinien für Windschutz.* Frankfurt-am-Main, Deutsche Landwirtschafts-Gesellschaft-Verlag, 1955.

Landsberg, H. E. "Controlled Climate (Outdoor and Indoor)," in J. Licht, ed., *Medical Climatology.* Physical Medical Library, v. 8. New Haven, Conn., Physical Medical Library, 1964.

Le Sueur, A. D. C. *Hedges, Shelterbelts and Screens.* London, Country Life, 1951.

Logginov, B. I. *Osnovy Polezashchitnogo Lesorazvedeniya (Principles of Field Protective Forestation).* All-Union Academy of Agricultural Science Translations. v. 3. Leningrad, 1941.

McCutchan, G., and W. W. Caudill. *An Experiment in Architectural Education Through Research.* Texas Engineering Experiment Station Research Report 32. College Station, Texas Engineering Experiment Station, 1952.

Meetham, A. R., and others. *Atmospheric Pollution: Its Origins and Prevention.* 3d rev. ed. New York, Pergamon Press, 1964.

Meldau, R. "Besondere lufttechnische Aufgaben der Industrie," *Staedtehygiene,* v. 3, no. 8, 1959.

Mikheilesku, V. "Schematic Topoclimate Map of Romania—Review of the Geology and Geography," Bucharest, Publishing House of the National Academy of Rumania, v. 3, 2, 1959.

Ministry of Agriculture, Fisheries and Food. *Shelterbelts for Farmland.* Fixed Equipment of the Farm, Leaflet 15. London, Her Majesty's Stationery Office, 1961.

Ministry of Housing and Local Government. *Trees in Town and City.* London, Her Majesty's Stationery Office, 1958.

Munns, E. N., and J. H. Stoeckeler. "How Are the Great Plains Shelterbelts?" *Journal of Forestry,* v. 44, no. 4, 1946.

Neuberger, H., C. L. Hosler and W. C. Kocmond. "Vegetation as Aerosol Filter." *Bioclimatology,* 2. Proceedings of the 3d International Congress on Bioclimatology. New York, 1967.

Olgyay, Victor. *Design With Climate.* Princeton, N.J., Princeton University Press, 1963.

Panfilov, Y. "A Contribution to the Problem of the Effect of the Shelterbelts on Wind Velocity on Steep Slopes," *Sovetska Agronomiska*, v. 1, no. 3, 1940.

———. "Shelterbelts on the Watershed Plateau of the Prairie Zone of the Volga Region." *Polezashtchitnye Polossy* (Shelterbelts) Report of the All-Union Scientific Research Institute for Improvement of Farmland by Forestation, v. 8, 1936. (In Russian, translation in English, U.S. Department of Agriculture Translation No. 7315).

Pinnard, T. S., and E. T. Wilkins. "Air Pollution in London and Its Smokeless Zones." A paper prepared for the Annual Conference of the National Society for Clean Air. London, *Llaudukno* (Conference held October 1-3, 1958).

Reifsnyder, W. E. "Windprofiles in a Small Isolated Forest Stand," *Forest Science*, v. 1, no. 6, 1927.

Searle, S. A., and L. P. Smith. *Weatherwise Gardening.* London, Blandford Press, 1958.

Smal'ko, Y. A. "Zony Vetrozasshchitnogo Vliyaniya lesnykh polos raznukh Konstruktsii" (Range of wind sheltering in forest strips of different structures). Leningrad, *Izvestiya Akademii Naukovi SSSR, Seriya geografisheskaya*, v. 18, no. 5, 1954 (English abstracts).

Smith, E. G. *The Feasibility of Using Models for Predetermining Natural Ventilation.* Texas Engineering Experiment Station Research Report 26. College Station, Texas Engineering Experiment Station, 1951.

Smith, E. G., B. H. Reed and H. D. Hodges. *The Measurement of Low Air Speeds by the Use of Titanium Tetrachloride.* Texas Engineering Experiment Station Research Report 25. College Station, Texas Engineering Experiment Station, 1951.

Stoeckler, Joseph H., and V. Ross Williams. "Windbreaks and Shelterbelts," in U.S. Department of Agriculture, *Yearbook of Agriculture.* Washington, D.C., U.S. Government Printing Office, 1949.

Sutton, O. G. *Atmospheric Turbulence.* London, Meuthen & Co., 1955.

———. "Note on the Variation of the Wind with Height," *The Quarterly Journal of the Royal Meteorological Society*, v. 58, no. 12, 1932.

Swimbank, W. C. *Turbulent Transfer in the Lower Atmosphere.* Proceedings of the Canberra Symposium 1956. Paris, United Nations Educational, Social, and Cultural Organization, 1958.

Tanaka, S. T., and others. "Studies on the Wind in Front and Back of the Shelter-Hedges," Tokyo, *Nogyo Kisho*, v. 8 (1955) 61-63; v. 9 (1954) 66-68; v. 10 (1954) 30-32; v. 11 (1955) 49-52, 91-94, 97-99; v. 12 (1956) 9-12, 73-78; v. 13 (1957) 7-8.

Thompson, F. L., W. C. Peck and A. P. Beard. "Air Conditions Close to the Ground and the Effect on Airplane Landings," *in* U.S. National Advisory Committee for Aeronautics, *Annual Report.* Washington, D.C., U.S. Government Printing Office, 1934.

Thornthwaite, C. W., and M. Halstead. "Note on the Variation of Wind with Height in the Layer Near the Ground," American Geophysical Union, *Transactions*, v. 23, 1942.

U.S. Department of Agriculture. *Shelterbelt Influence on Great Plains Field Environment and Crops.* U.S. Department of Agriculture Report 62, October 1962.

Van der Linde, R. J. and J. P. M. Woudenberg. "On the Microclimatic Properties of Sheltered Areas," *Journal of the Netherlands Meteorological Institute*, v. 151, no. 102, 1960.

Van Eimern, J., ed. *Windbreaks and Shelterbelts.* World Meteorological Technical Note 59. Geneva, Switzerland, World Meteorological Organization, 1964.

———. "Kleinklimatische Geländeaufnahme in Quickbom-Holstein," *Annalen der Meteorologie* v. 4, 1951.

Vezey, E. E. *The Feasibility of Using Models for Predetermining Natural Lighting.* Texas Engineering Experiment Station Research Report 21. College Station, Texas Engineering Experiment Station, 1951.

Von Nageli, W. *Proceedings of the Congress of the International Union of Forestry Research Organizations.* London, International Union of Forestry Research Organizations, 1953.

———. "Untersuchungen über die Windverhältnisse im Bereich Windschutzstreifen," Zurich, *Mitteilungen der Schweizerischem Anstalt für das forstliche Versuchswesen*, v. 23, no. 8, 1943 and v. 24, no. 2, 1946.

———. "Untersuchungen über die Windverhältnisse im Bereich von Schilfrohrwanden," Zurich, *Ebenda*, v. 29, no. 3, 1953.

Wainwright, C. W. K., and M. J. G. Wilson. "Atmospheric Pollution in a London Park," *International Journal of Air and Water Pollution*, v. 6, 1962.

Weiner, S. I. "Solar Orientation Application of Local Wind

Factors," *Progressive Architecture*, February 1955.

White, Robert F. *Effects of Landscape Development on the Natural Ventilation of Buildings and Their Adjacent Areas.* Texas Engineering Experiment Station Research Report 45. College Station, Texas Engineering Experiment Station, 1945.

Whitten, A. J. "The Ventilation of Oxford Circus," *Weather*, v. 11, no. 8, 1956.

"Wind Tests: Which Fence is Best?" *How to Build Fences and Gates.* Menlo Park, Calif., Lane Publishing Company, 1951.

Woodrow, A. D., and T. H. Dickey. "A Study of a Topographic Effect on Wind in the Arctic," *Journal of Meteorology*, v. 18, sec. 6, 1961.

Woodruff, N. P. *Shelterbelt and Surface Barrier Effects.* Technical Bulletin 77. Manhattan, Kans., Agricultural Experiment Station, 1954.

Woodruff, N. P., and A. W. Zingg. "Wind Tunnel Studies of Shelterbelt Models," *Journal of Forestry*, v. 51, no. 3, 1953.

————. *Wind Tunnel Studies of Fundamental Problems Related to Windbreaks.* Soil Conservation Service Technical Publication 112. Washington, D.C., U.S. Department of Agriculture, 1952.

Yaglou, C. P., and W. E. Miller. "Effective Temperature with Clothing," American Society of Heating and Ventilating Engineers, *Transactions*, v. 31, no. 717, 1925.

Young, F. D. "Frost and the Prevention of Frost Damage," *Journal of Marine Research*, v. 12, no. 2, 1948.

Precipitation Control

Beale, H. W. "The Penetration of Rainfall Through Hardwood and Softwood Forest Canopy," *Ecology*, v. 15, no. 5, 1934.

Blanford, H. F. "On the Influence of Indian Forests on the Rainfall," *Journal of the Asiatic Society of Bengal*, v. 56, II, 1887.

Caborn, J. M. *Shelterbelts and Windbreaks.* London, Faber and Faber, 1965.

Daigo, Y., and E. Maruyama. "Experimental Studies of Windbreaks for Protection from Frost Damage," *Memoirs of Industrial Meteorology*, v. 2, no. 3, 1956.

Flaegle, R. G. "A Theory of Fog Formation," New Haven, *Journal of Marine Research*, v. 12, no. 8, 1949.

Fukutoumi, T. "Effect of Ground Temperature Upon the Thickness of Snow Cover," *Low Temperature Science*, v. 9, no. 7, 1953.

Geiger, Rudolph. *The Climate Near the Ground.* Cambridge, Mass., Harvard University Press, 1950.

Helvey, J. D., and J. H. Patric. "Canopy and Litter Interception of Rainfall by Hardwoods of Eastern United States," *Water Resources Research*, v. 1, no. 3, 1965.

Jaenicke, A. J., and M. H. Foerster. "The Influence of a Western Yellow Pine Forest on the Accumulation and Melting of Snow," *Monthly Weather Review*, v. 43, no. 8, 1953.

Kittredge, J. "Influences of Forests on Snow in the Ponderosa-Sugar Pine-Fir Zone of the Central Sierra Nevada," *Hilgardia*, v. 1, no. 2, 1926.

Lacy, R. E. "Distribution of Rainfall Around a House," *The Meteorological Magazine*, v. 80, no. 8, 1951.

Linskens, H. F. "Niederschlagsmessungen unter verschiedenen Baukronentypen im belaubten v. unbelaubten Zustand," *Berichte der deutschen Botanischen Gesellschaft*, v. 64, no. 1, 1951.

Moran, B. "Influence of Undergrowth on the Relative Humidity of the Atmospheric Surface Layers," *Tschechoslow Akademia Margina Sbornic*, v. 21, no. 11, 1949. (Referred to in American Meteorological Society, *Meteorological Abstracts and Bibliography*, v. 8. Boston, American Meteorological Society, 1957.)

McAdie, A. G. "Studies in Frost Protection—Effect of Mixing the Air," in U.S. Department of Agriculture, *Monthly Weather Review*, v. 40, Washington, D.C., U.S. Department of Agriculture, 1912.

Monteith, J. L. "The Effect of Grass-Length on Snow Melting," *Weather*, v. 11, no. 3, 1959.

"Nature's Own Cooling System," *Nursery Business*, September-October 1970.

Olson, Harold E. "Landscape for Snowdrift Control," *Park Maintenance*, March 1963.

Ooura, H. "The Capture of Frost Particles by the Forest," *Journal of Agricultural Meteorology*, v. 4, no. 12, supplement, 1952.

Ovington, J. D. "A Comparison of Rainfall in Different Woods," *Forestry*, v. 27, no. 4, 1954.

Rowe, P. B., and J. M. Hendrix. "Interception of Rain and Snow by Second Growth Ponderosa Pine," American Geophysical Union, *Transactions*, v. 32, no. 2, 1951.

Stoeckler, J. H., and E. J. Dortignac. "Snowdrifts as a Factor in Growth and Longevity of Shelterbelts in the Great Plains," *Ecology*, v. 22, no. 5, 1941.

Suzuki, S. "The Nocturnal Cooling of Plant Leaves and Hoar-frost Deposited Thereon," *Geophysical Magazine*, v. 25, no. 10, 1954.

Takeda, K. "Rainfall in Forest," *Journal of Agricultural Meteorology*, v. 29, no. 7, 1951.

Trimble, G. R., and S. Weitzman. "Effects of a Hardwood Forest Canopy on Rainfall Intensities," American Geophysical Union, *Transactions*, v. 35, no. 6, 1954.

Wexler, A. *Humidity and Moisture*. Washington, D.C., U.S. Weather Bureau, 1955.

Temperature Control

Bernatzky, Aloys. "Climatic Influences of the Greens and City Planning," *Anthos*, v. 5, no. 1, 1966.

Bornstein, Robert D. "Observation of the Urban Heat Island Effect in New York City," *Journal of Applied Meteorology*, v. 7, no. 6, 1968.

Brengelmann, G., and A. C. Brown. "Temperature Regulation," in T. C. Ruch and H. D. Patton, eds., *Physiology and Biophysics*. 19th ed. Philadelphia, Saunders, 1965.

Chandler, T. J. "London's Urban Climate," *Geographical Journal*, v. 128, no. 11, 1962.

Christi, H. R. "Vertical Temperature Gradients in a Beech Forest in Central Ohio," *Ohio Journal of Sciences*, v. 52, no. 6, 1952.

Duckworth, Fowler S., and James S. Sandberg. "The Effect of Cities Upon Horizontal and Vertical Temperature Gradients," *American Meteorological Society Bulletin*, v. 35, no. 4, 1954.

Linskens, H. F. "Niederschlagsmessungen unter verschiedenen Baukronentypen im belaubten u. unbelaubten zustand," *Berichte der deutschen Botanischen Gesellschaft*, v. 64, no. 1, 1951.

Muterich, A. *Bericht über die Untersuchung der Einwirkung des Waldes auf die Menge der Niederschlage*. Neudamm, Neumann, 1903.

Olgyay, Victor and Aladar. *Design With Climate*. Princeton, N. J., Princeton University Press, 1963.

Van der Linde, R. J. "On the Microclimatic Properties of Sheltered Areas," *Journal of the Netherlands Meteorological Institute*, v. 102, no. 2, 1950.

Waterhouse, F. L. "Microclimatological Profiles in Grass Cover in Relation to Biological Problems," *The Quarterly Journal of the Royal Meteorological Society*, v. 81, no. 5, 1955.

We wish to express our appreciation to the many persons who have kindly given criticism and advice during the preparation of this book, particularly to Dr. Robert Linn, chief scientist; Dr. Theodore Sudia, senior scientist; and David G. Wright, landscape architect of the National Park Service. This volume could not have been successfully compiled without the invaluable aid and assistance of the personnel of the Service Center of the National Park Service. Grateful acknowledgement is made to James G. Kiryakakis, Naomi L. Hunt, Judith Babb, William B. Hall, Pamela J. LaRocque, Elliott Blankenship, Mary Matkovcik, Carol Watson, Dale W. Rennoll, Ruth Wimmer, Patrick A. Hurley, and others. The typography and design of this book are by R. Donald Carguil.

MB-3 -2165

☆U. S. GOVERNMENT PRINTING OFFICE : 1972 O - 468-199